Mrs. Hunt

Mrs. Hurt

1000 FACTS ON
ROCKS & MINERALS

Barnes & Noble Publishing, Inc.
122 Fifth Avenue
New York, NY 10011

ISBN-13: 978-0-7607-6810-5
ISBN-10: 0-7607-6810-2

Printed and bound in China

06 07 08 09 MCH 10 9 8 7 6 5 4 3 2

Library of Congress Cataloging-in-Publication Data available upon request.

Editorial Director: Belinda Gallagher

Assistant Editor: Hannah Todd

Editorial Assistant: Bethanie Bourne

Designer: Tom Slemmings

Picture Research Manager: Liberty Newton

Picture Researcher: Laura Faulder

Production Manager: Elizabeth Brunwin

Indexer: Jane Parker

Americanization: Jenni Rainford

Scanning and Reprographics: Anthony Cambray,
Mike Coupe, Ian Paulyn

1000 FACTS ON
ROCKS &
MINERALS

Chris & Helen Pellant
Consultant: Keith Ambrose

BARNES & NOBLE

NEW YORK

Contents

Contents

Contents

What is a rock?

- **A rock is an aggregate** (mixture) of mineral particles. It may be made of loose sand (sandstone) or sticky clay (mudstone), fossil and fossil debris (limestone), or mineral crystals welded together (igneous and high grade metamorphic rocks).

- **Scientists classify rocks** into three main groups—igneous, sedimentary, and metamorphic.

- **Rocks began to form** as soon as the original molten (liquid) Earth started to cool around 4,000 million years ago.

- **The first rocks to form** were igneous rocks. These crystallized from molten magma (underground) or lava (on the surface).

- **Rocks form in a cycle.** Igneous rocks are weathered and eroded and formed into sedimentary rocks. These may be altered by metamorphism (the effect of extreme heat or pressure) and eventually, if they are buried very deep in the Earth's crust, they melt and become igneous rocks again.

- **The age of rocks** can be worked out by studying the fossils they contain or the breakdown of radioactive elements contained in them. This is called radiometric dating.

- **As soon as the Earth's atmosphere** had begun to develop, around 2,000 million years ago, weathering and erosion began to break down the early igneous rocks to make sediments.

> ...·FASCINATING FACT·...
> The oldest rocks to be radiometrically
> dated are over 3,900 million years old.

● **Metamorphic rocks** are created when earlier-formed rocks are changed by heat from magma or lava, or by pressure and heat deep underground.

● **Rocks are being formed** all the time. The mud and sand on the beach or in a riverbed may become a sedimentary rock.

◄ *This cliff face shows layers of sedimentary sandstone at the top. Below these there is a narrow layer of very pale metamorphic rock and at the bottom an uneven mass of igneous dolerite.*

9

What are igneous rocks?

- **Geologists** sometimes call igneous rocks primary rocks because they form from molten material that originates deep in the Earth's crust.

- **Igneous rocks** can be distinguished from other rocks because they are made of a mosaic of mineral crystals, usually without layers.

- **The crystals** in igneous rocks are usually welded together.

- **Igneous rocks** occur in many different structures, both underground (intrusive) and on the surface (extrusive).

- **Intrusive** igneous rocks form underground in large masses called batholiths, and relatively small intrusions, for example, sills and dykes.

- **Extrusive** igneous rocks build volcanoes. These may have large rocky craters or be mountains of ash and dust.

- **Igneous rocks** are the best rocks for radiometric dating because the crystals in them formed at a definite time in the past. These crystals may not have altered since their formation, so an accurate date can often be obtained. Radiometric dating is most accurate if the rocks used are fresh and unweathered.

▶ *In a thin slice of granite magnified many times, the crystals are clearly seen. The gray crystals are quartz and feldspar and the brighter colors are mica.*

10

- **Basalt** is a volcanic igneous rock that makes up more of the Earth's crust than any other rock. It covers the vast ocean basins.

- **Granite**, an intrusive igneous rock that forms deep underground, makes up much of the Earth's continental crust.

- **Some igneous rocks**, such as granite and dolerite, are very hard and durable and are quarried for use in road surfaces.

▼ *Crater Lake in Oregon, is the remains of a collapsed volcano called a caldera. The small cone forms Wizard Island.*

How igneous rocks vary

- **Igneous rocks** differ from each other in two main ways—what they are made of and the size of their crystals.

- **The composition** of an igneous rock is not usually complex, and consists of very few minerals.

- **One main group** of igneous rocks, which geologists call felsic (acid) rocks, is made largely of three easily identified minerals—quartz, feldspar, and mica.

▼ *Lava can erupt in a violent, frothy mass, containing a lot of gas. When it cools, it is full of gas-bubble holes.*

▶ *These brightly colored lumps of lava, each a few inches across, are called rainbow slag. This volcanic rock occurs in southern Iceland.*

- **Acid rocks** are usually pale-colored and not very heavy.

- **Another important group** is made of feldspar, olivine, and pyroxene, with only a small amount of quartz. These are called mafic (basic) rocks.

- **Basic rocks** are generally dark-colored and heavier than you would expect when picked up.

- **If an igneous rock** solidifies as magma cools deep underground, the crystals it is made of will often be large enough to see with the naked eye. Geologists refer to these rocks as coarse-grained.

- **Igneous rocks** that solidify as lava cools on the Earth's surface have very small mineral crystals. A microscope may be required to see them. These rocks are fine-grained.

- **Sometimes magma** or lava cools in two stages—one deep underground and the other on, or near, the surface. If this happens, the rock will contain some large crystals and some smaller ones.

- **Volcanic rocks** include a whole range of fragments blown to bits by an eruption. Examples are dust, ash, and pumice.

Granite

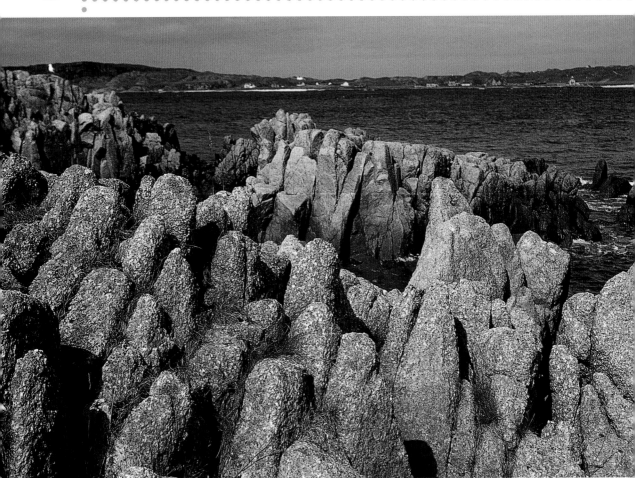

▲ *This granite on the Isle of Mull, western Scotland, has been weathered along its vertical joints. The pink color results from large amounts of feldspar in the rock.*

- **Granite** is one of the best-known igneous rocks because of its colorful crystalline appearance. Polished slabs are used to decorate buildings.

- **It is a coarse-grained** igneous rock with crystals that are easily seen by the naked eye. They are generally more than 0.02 in (5 mm) across. Granite also contains white or pink crystals of feldspar and black or silvery white mica.

- **Other minerals** found in granite, which don't affect its classification, are called accessory minerals. These include pyrite, tourmaline, and apatite.

- **Granite contains** a large amount of quartz. This common mineral is off white or gray, greasy-looking, and very hard.

- **Granite forms** deep in the Earth's crust in large chambers of molten magma called batholiths. The magma cools very slowly, often taking many millions of years, which enables the crystals in granite to grow to a large size.

- **For granite to be exposed** at the surface, many thousands of feet of rock have to be weathered and eroded. Rocks may also be pushed up by mountain building processes before granite is exposed on the Earth's surface.

- **Granite** is not as hard and durable as many people think. It is easily weathered, especially in humid climates, and decomposes to sand and clay.

- **In the area around** a mass of granite, there is a region of metamorphism where heat from the magma has changed the original rocks.

- **In the area** near to a granite batholith it my be possible to mine for tin, coppper, lead, zinc, and other minerals.

Batholiths

- **A batholith** is a very large mass of igneous rock that was originally magma.

- **Batholiths** are commonly formed deep in the roots of mountain chains and may be many tens of miles in diameter.

- **In Britain**, a batholith exists under much of Cornwall and reaches out under the sea to the Scilly Isles. This covers an area of 40 mi (65 km) by 25 mi (40 km). Many batholiths are larger than this.

- **Before the giant mass** of magma in the batholith was intruded (forced in), there was other rock in that part of the Earth's crust. Geologists have puzzled over what happened to the original rock. It is believed that some of it was melted and incorporated into the magma.

- **Granite magma** itself may be the result of the melting of other rock at great depth.

- **Sills and dykes** may stretch upward from some batholiths.

- **Most batholiths** are made of granite. Some contain other coarse-grained igneous rocks like syenite and gabbro.

- **Even when the rock** in a batholith has been crystalline for millions of years, heat will still rise through it from a great depth. This heat may be trapped if clay and other rock have formed later.

- **Scientists** have discovered that this heat could be used to produce electricity in a safe, clean way.

...FASCINATING FACT...
The batholith in the Andes mountains of Peru covers an area 994 mi (1600 km) by 118 (190 km).

▼ *A batholith is a gigantic mass of magma formed deep below a mountain range. Small offshoots of magma may rise from it higher into the Earth's crust. Lumps of rock called xenoliths (see p22) may be present in the batholith.*

Batholith

Xenolith

Gabbro

- **Gabbro** is a dark igneous rock. It is made of quite large crystals and has a speckled appearance.

- **Gabbro** forms as large masses of magma cool, as granite does, but it is made of different minerals. Because it cools slowly, it has large, easily visible crystals.

- **Rather than occurring** in batholiths, gabbro is commonly found in thick sheets of igneous rock.

- **Feldpsar and pyroxene** are the two main minerals in gabbro, but it also has a small amount of quartz—less than 10 percent.

- **Feldspar is a pale mineral**, often occurring in thin crystals in gabbro, while pyroxene is almost black, giving the rock its speckled appearance.

- **Compared with granite**, gabbro is a very dark-colored rock, and is also noticeably heavier. This is because it contains a large amount of pyroxene, which is a dense mineral.

- **A mineral called olivine** is sometimes found in gabbro. This is a green or brownish mineral rich in iron and magnesium, which crystallizes at very high temperatures.

- **Gabbro** mainly forms in the Earth's crust beneath the basalts of the ocean floors but can also occur on continents. Granite typically occurs in a continental setting.

- **Some famous masses** of gabbro are at Bushveldt in South Africa and Stillwater, Montana.

- **In Britain**, the Cuillin Hills on the Isle of Skye, in western Scotland are largely made of gabbro, which weathers into jagged peaks.

Gabbro

▲ *The jagged gabbro peaks of the Cuillins seen across Loch Slapin on the Isle of Skye, U.K.*

19

Pegmatite

▲ *This intrusion of pegmatite is full of large, pink feldspar crystals. It has cut into dark-colored metamorphic rock.*

● **Pegmatite** is an igneous rock formed deep underground and made up of very large crystals. These may be over 1.2 in (3 cm) long. In some pegmatite rocks, giant crystals over 3.3 ft (1 m) long have been discovered.

- **For such large crystals to form**, the magma must cool very slowly, allowing the crystals a long time to develop.

- **Pegmatite** occurs in sheets and other structures, often around the margins of large scale intrusions.

- **Sills and dykes** of pegmatite also occur in many areas of very old gneiss.

- **Usually**, pegmatite has a similar composition to granite, containing mainly feldspar, mica, and quartz. However, gabbro and syenite pegmatites are not unknown.

- **Pegmatite** generally crystallizes from magma and other high-temperature fluids, which are rich in many rare elements. These include niobium, tantalum, lithium, and tungsten. This makes some pegmatites economically valuable.

- **Among the extra minerals** that are often found in pegmatites are tourmaline, topaz, fluorite, apatite, and cassiterite.

- **Radioactive elements**, such as autunite and torbernite, also occur in pegmatite.

- **Some pegmatites** have an attractive appearance called graphic texture. This looks rather like ancient writing and is created by quartz and feldspar crystals merging in the rock.

> ...FASCINATING FACT...
> A crystal of the mineral beryl, nearly 19.7 ft (6 m) long, and a spodumene crystal over 49ft (15 m) long, were found in a pegmatite in South Dakota.

Xenolith

- **The word "xenolith"** comes from the Greek *xenos*, which means "stranger" and *lithos*, meaning "stone."

- **These "stranger stones"** are found around the margins of many igneous intrusions, where magma has melted and forced its way into other rocks. They may also be found in lava.

- **They are lumps of rock** that have been broken off and engulfed by the igneous rock, so are strangers in their new location.

- **Xenoliths** often appear as dark, rounded, or irregular rocks set into granite or another igneous rock.

- **Near the very edge** of the igneous intrusion, a xenolith will not have been heated too much by the magma and so keeps many of its original features.

- **Xenoliths** found some feet into the igneous rock will have been altered considerably and metamorphosed. They may even have crystals in them similar to those in the igneous rock.

- **Xenoliths** help geologists to work out the types of rock the magma passed through, as it was being intruded or erupted.

- **In some places** blocks of the very lowest crustal rocks have been brought to the surface by rising magma. These xenoliths allow geologists to study rocks not normally seen on the surface.

- **In the diamond-bearing rocks** around Kimberly, South Africa, xenoliths that may be derived from the Earth's mantle (the region beneath the crust) are found.

- **Large amounts of xenolith rock** caught up in magma may react with it and change its composition.

▼ *Large, dark xenoliths can be easily seen in this eroded mass of igneous diorite. They were surrounded by molten magma and partly changed by its heat.*

Syenite

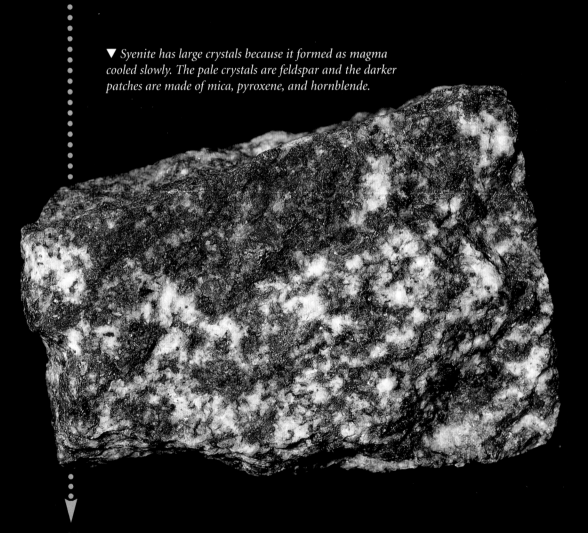

▼ *Syenite has large crystals because it formed as magma cooled slowly. The pale crystals are feldspar and the darker patches are made of mica, pyroxene, and hornblende.*

- **Syenite** is an intrusive igneous rock that has formed by the cooling of magma deep in the Earth's crust.

- **Because of the slow cooling** associated with the high temperatures at great depth, syenite has large crystals and is a coarse-grained rock. The crystals can be seen with the naked eye.

- **Syenite** may look rather like granite, but by studying the minerals it contains, differences can be seen.

- **Syenite** will usually appear darker-colored than granite, but not as dark as gabbro. Some syenites may be pink or gray or tinged with violet.

- **One well-known** type of syenite is called larvikite. It is from Norway and is commonly cut into slabs and polished to make a pearly blue-green ornamental stone. This has been used as a facing stone on many buildings throughout the U.K.

- **As well as occurring** in large intrusions, syenite is also found in sills and dykes. These rocks tend to have smaller crystals.

- **Many syenites** have large crystals set into a finer mass, giving an attractive appearance. This is called a porphyritic texture.

- **As well as feldspar and quartz**, syenite can contain hornblende, pyroxene, and the dark mica biotite. This composition contains features of both granite and gabbro.

- **Microsyenite** is an igneous rock with the composition of syenite but contains smaller crystals.

- **Rhomb porphyry** is a type of microsyenite found commonly in Norway. Pebbles of it, which have been carried by ice sheets across the North Sea area, are often found on the east coast of England.

Dykes and sills

- **Dykes and sills** are called minor igneous intrusions because they are of moderate to small size.

- **Both intrusions** are sheets of igneous rock and are commonly made of rocks such as dolerite that have cooled quite quickly and are fine grained.

- **They are** usually measured in feet, being anything from seven or eight metres in thickness to a few hundred.

- **A dyke** is very often a vertical sheet of dark rock cutting across existing strata (layers). Geologists call this a discordant intrusion.

- **The magma** forming the dyke will have risen into a fracture in the overlying rocks.

- **Dykes are often found** in great numbers, or swarms. One such swarm occurs in the Inner Hebrides across southern Scotland and stretches into the north of England.

- **A sill**, in contrast, follows the rock structures in the area where it is intruded. This is called a concordant intrusion. In sedimentary rocks, they are generally intruded along bedding planes.

- **Because they are small** structures giving out little heat, there is usually only a small metamorphic effect on neighboring rocks.

- **Like many lava flows**, sills may form vertical columns of rock that results from the way the magma has cooled. This is known as columnar jointing.

> ...FASCINATING FACT...
> On the Isle of Arran, Scotland, 525 dykes occur within a distance of
> 15 mi (24 km). These have stretched the Earth's crust by 7 percent.

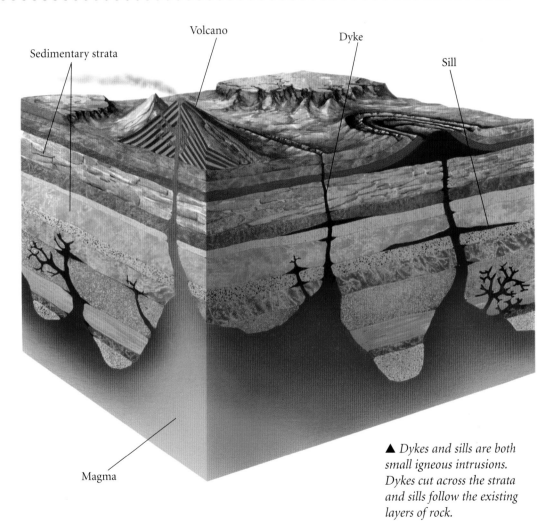

Volcano

Dyke

Sill

Sedimentary strata

Magma

▲ *Dykes and sills are both small igneous intrusions. Dykes cut across the strata and sills follow the existing layers of rock.*

27

Dolerite

- **Dolerite** is a dark-colored igneous rock, often with an overall speckled appearance.

- **The speckled surface** results from the minerals it contains. These are light-colored feldspar and black pyroxene. There is also a small amount of pale gray quartz. This is the same composition as gabbro and basalt.

- **Dolerite** may contain the green or brownish mineral called olivine.

- **It is possible** to see its crystals with the naked eye, but to study them in detail a strong hand lens is needed. Geologists refer to this type of rock as being medium-grained.

- **Dolerite** commonly occurs in small igneous intrusions, such as sills and dykes, where magma has cooled much more rapidly than in a batholith.

- **Rounded vertical masses** of dolerite may be the necks of old volcanoes. These remain after the lava and ash of the volcano have been eroded.

- **Dolerite-forming magma** originates very low in the Earth's crust or in the upper mantle. The rock is generally associated with thin oceanic crust rather than areas of thick continental crust.

- **Dolerite** is a dense, heavy rock mainly because it contains minerals that are rich in iron.

- **American geologists** use the term diabase for this type of rock.

- **Dolerite** is a very hard and durable rock. It is extensively quarried for road stone, railroad ballast, and other uses.

◀ *Because dolerite forms from magma that has cooled relatively quickly, its crystals are not easy to see. A powerful hand lens would be needed to see the crystals in detail.*

Serpentinite

- **Serpentinite** is unlike many igneous rocks in a number of vital ways. It is thought to be formed by the chemical alteration of other igneous rocks.

- **It often contains** very attractive colors, such as shades of green and red. These colors often make veins through the rock.

- **Because it is easily cut**, shaped, and polished, serpentinite is often used ornamentally. This is especially true in areas where it is a common rock, such as around the Lizard peninsula in Cornwall, U.K.

- **Serpentinite** is made largely of a variety of "serpentine" minerals. These include chrysotile and antigorite, which are both silicate minerals with a slippery, soapy feel, and fibrous structure.

- **Chrysotile** is a source of asbestos, once used for its insulating properties.

- **Serpentinites** contain virtually no quartz, but can contain a number of silicate minerals, such as garnet, mica, hornblende, and pyroxene.

- **It is generally believed** that serpentinites were originally dense, heavy rocks related to the lowest parts of the Earth's crust. These were rich in minerals such as olivine, and have been much altered by the addition of water.

- **In some examples**, there is little indication as to what the original rock may have been because the serpentinization is so extreme.

- **Serpentinites** are found in many areas including, Montana, Cornwall, Anglesey, and Shetland (U.K.), New Zealand, and New South Wales (Australia).

- **Serpentine minerals** are also found in a group of meteorites called carbonaceous chondrites.

▲ *The coast of the Lizard Peninsula in Cornwall, U.K., where serpentinite occurs.*

Volcanoes

- **A volcano** is an opening in the Earth's crust through which lava escapes.

- **Depending on the type** of lava and other volcanic materials, the volcano may be a low, gently sloping structure or a steep, cone-shaped mountain.

- **Some volcanoes** have a single opening. These are called central volcanoes. Others have a number of vents and are called fissure volcanoes.

- **Volcanoes** from which basalt lava erupts are not as violent as those that produce rhyolite and andesite lavas. Basaltic lava has a higher temperature and a less sticky silica than rhyolite and andesite lavas. This means that it flows easily away from the vent.

- **The Hawaiian**, or shield, volcanoes are made of basalt. They have large craters and low domes that spread many tens of miles. The base of Mauna Loa in Hawaii is 70 mi (112 km) in diameter.

- **Strombolian volcanoes**, named after the island of Stromboli to the north of Sicily, are classic cone shapes. Eruptions can be violent. As well as lava there are layers of ash and dust.

- **Vesuvian volcanoes**, named after Mt. Vesuvius in Italy, erupt only once every ten or more years. The lava is sticky and plugs the vent, causing violent eruptions.

- **Pelean volcanoes**, named after Mt. Pelee in Martinique, are among the most violent. These erupt sticky, silica-rich lava, which often solidifies in the volcano. A great pressure then builds up as more lava tries to get through, and much of the volcano is blown apart by the eruption.

- **Volcanoes** can be very destructive. In 1883, Krakatoa in Java erupted, sending a huge dust cloud around the Earth's atmosphere. This affected the climate for three years. Over 36,000 people died as a result of the eruption.

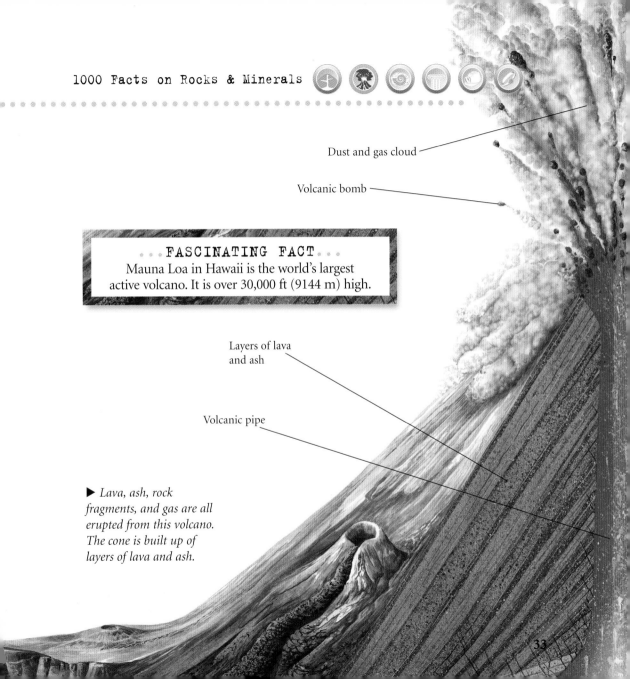

Dust and gas cloud

Volcanic bomb

...FASCINATING FACT...
Mauna Loa in Hawaii is the world's largest
active volcano. It is over 30,000 ft (9144 m) high.

Layers of lava
and ash

Volcanic pipe

▶ *Lava, ash, rock
fragments, and gas are all
erupted from this volcano.
The cone is built up of
layers of lava and ash.*

33

Where volcanoes occur

- **The distribution of volcanoes** is closely linked to lines of weakness in the Earth's crust and its varying thickness.

- **In ocean areas**, the crust is less than 6 mi (10 km) thick, but below the great continents it may be 36 mi (60 km) thick. Lava can more easily escape to the surface where the crust is thin.

▼ *On the deep ocean bed where slabs of the Earth's crust move apart, lava erupts to form a range of underwater volcanic mountains.*

Sea level

Ocean plate

Mid-ocean ridge

Central canyon

Ridges are lower and older away from center

- **The Earth's crust** and the uppermost part of the underlying layer, the mantle, make up the lithosphere. This is divided into a number of plates.

- **The lithospheric plates** are internally solid but constantly move. Some collide, others move away from each other. It is along these plate boundaries that volcanic activity is concentrated.

- **The "Ring of Fire"** around the Pacific Ocean has been studied for many years as many of the world's volcanoes are located in this region. The Pacific Ocean floor is the largest of Earth's plates and around its edges are weaknesses where erupting basaltic lavas can well up to the surface.

- **The volcanoes** in Southeast Asia, Japan, South and North America are all part of the Ring of Fire.

- **In the Atlantic**, the situation is different. There are two major plates making up this ocean basin, which are moving away from each other. The Mid-Atlantic Ridge, which is mainly below sea level, is a line of active volcanoes.

- **In Iceland**, the Mid-Atlantic Ridge reaches above sea level. This large island is made almost entirely of volcanic rock.

- **There are other regions** where eruptions are caused by plates moving apart from each other. The African Rift Valley is one place where this process is beginning—volcanoes such as Kilimanjaro occur.

- **The Hawaiian volcanoes** are in the center of the Pacific plate, forming a chain of islands. They lie above a plume of hot material rising from the base of the crust.

Basalt

- **Basalt** makes up more of the Earth's crust than any other rock. Beneath a thin layer of sediment, it covers the ocean floor. More than 90 percent of the volcanic rocks found on the Earth are basalt.

- **Basalt** is a volcanic rock that often erupts non-violently and can flow great distances.

- **It is a dark-colored rock** and its crystals can rarely be seen on its surface without a microscope. Basalt is what geologists call a fine-grained rock.

- **The composition** of basalt is the same as that of gabbro and dolerite. It contains small crystals of feldspar, pyroxene, and common olivine with a small amount of quartz.

- **When it erupts**, basalt lava contains much gas. As the rock cools, gas-bubble hollows are left in the solid rock. These are called vesicles, and give the rock a rough texture.

- **Many fine mineral specimens**, including agate, develop in the vesicles, often long after the rock has cooled.

- **Basalt** is a dense, heavy rock. It contains iron-rich minerals, which because of their magnetism, have been of great use in working out the movement of the Earth's plates.

- **Basalt lava flows** often develop amazingly regular six-sided columns when cool. The Giant's Causeway in Northern Ireland is a fine example of this feature (see p42).

- **Rocks recovered** from the Moon are basaltic. These contain very similar minerals to those found in terrestrial basalts.

▶ The flow lines can be clearly seen on the surface of this basalt in Iceland.

...FASCINATING FACT...

In the Deccan area of north-west India, basalt lava flows reach a thickness of nearly 6,562 ft (2000 m) and cover about 30 percent of the area of peninsular India.

Obsidian

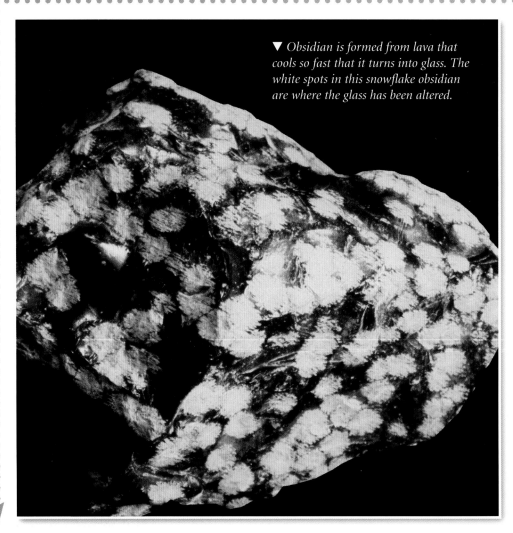

▼ *Obsidian is formed from lava that cools so fast that it turns into glass. The white spots in this snowflake obsidian are where the glass has been altered.*

- **When lava erupts** rapidly onto the Earth's surface, it is suddenly in an environment a thousand degrees cooler than the one it was in underground.

- **Such a rapid temperature** change causes the lava to freeze and solidify rapidly. The rock formed may have a glassy surface with no crystals visible.

- **Obsidian** is a rock that is formed under these conditions, and it contains no real crystals.

- **With the help** of microscopes and chemical analysis, geologists have found that obsidian is related to granite in composition and to another volcanic rock called rhyolite.

- **Pitchstone** is a rock that is rather like obsidian, but contains more crystalline material and its surface is more like pitch, or tar.

- **When broken**, obsidian has a very sharp, curved surface. This is called a conchoidal (shelllike) fracture.

- **Its sharp fracture** has been exploited by primitive people for making weapons and other implements, as it can be easily and accurately shaped.

- **Snowflake obsidian** is an attractive rock covered with small white patches. These occur where the volcanic glass has deteriorated. This rock is often cut and polished.

- **Obsidian is a well-known rock**, but is not very common. Hecla in Iceland and Obsidian Cliff in Yellowstone National Park, are famous locations.

> ...FASCINATING FACT...
> The most striking feature of obsidian is
> that it looks just like a piece of black glass.

Tuff and bombs

- **As well as lava**, volcanoes erupt other material. Most of this is broken rock, dust, ash, and volcanic bombs.

- **Ash and dust** from a volcano may be thrown high into the atmosphere. Much of this material, especially the larger fragments, falls near the volcano.

- **When it has settled** on the ground and hardened into rock, this material is called tuff. Tuff may have features of sedimentary rocks, such as layers or strata. Ash that has settled in the sea may contain fossils of shellfish.

- **Ignimbrite** is a type of tuff in which the fragments are welded together, partly by quartz droplets. They are erupted from very violent Peleean volcanoes.

- **When Mt. Pelee** on Martinique erupted in 1902, an ignimbrite flow covered the town of St. Pierre, 5 mi (8 km) away, in a few minutes. The 30,000 inhabitants were buried under the welded tuff, which reached a temperature of nearly 1,832°F (1000°C).

▼ *Thin strands of lava called Pelee's hair form when the lava is blown by the wind.*

- **As droplets** and larger lumps of lava are flung into the air, volcanic bombs form. The red hot lava may spin as it falls back toward the ground, and so may cool in an elongated spindle shape.

- **Breadcrust bombs** are larger chunks of lava around which a skin, or crust, forms. The molten lava inside releases gas and the skin expands and cracks, giving the appearance of a loaf of bread.

- **Bombs** usually have a vesicular texture, being riddled with gas-bubble cavities.

- **In Hawaii**, a lava spray is forced through very small openings and blown into strands by the wind. The very thin hairlike glassy material is called Pelee's hair. Pelee is a mythical lady who is said to live inside the volcano.

▶ *Volcanic bombs are lumps of molten lava flung high into the air by a violent eruption.*

...FASCINATING FACT...
In 1815 the volcano Tabora, in Indonesia, erupted with such force that dust was blown into the atmosphere and carried worldwide. The dust masked the Sun and caused 1816 to be called "the year without summer."

Rock columns

- **In many parts of the world** there are famous igneous rock formations where the rock is in almost perfect vertical columns. These include The Giant's Causeway (Antrim, Northern Ireland), Waikato Dam, (North Island, New Zealand), and Svartifoss waterfall (Iceland).

- **The columns** may be many tens of feet high and can be perfectly symmetrical and usually six-sided.

- **The igneous rock** involved is very often basalt, although dolerite, rhyolite, and welded tuff may also form columns.

- **Columnar structures** are seen best in lava flows, but they also form less perfectly in sills.

- **Sills and lava flows** have vertical columns as they cool from the base and top. In a dyke, columns may develop horizontally as the rock cools from its vertical edges.

- **When a lake or pond** dries out, the wet mud on its bed shrinks into a pattern of polygonal cracks. Igneous rocks behave like this but in a more regular way.

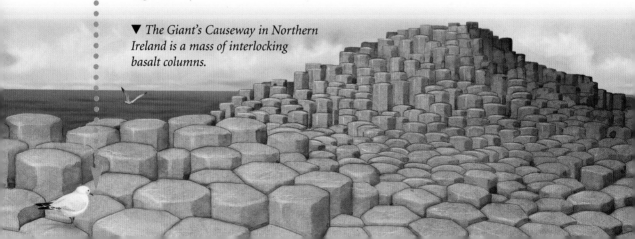

▼ *The Giant's Causeway in Northern Ireland is a mass of interlocking basalt columns.*

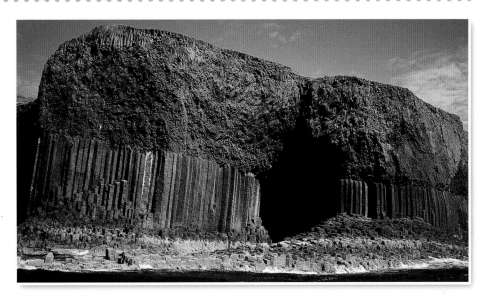

▲ *The vertical columns on the Isle of Staffa, Scotland, have a mass of uneven lava above them. The dark opening is Fingal's Cave.*

- **The processes** that allow such regular shapes to form in cooling rock probably involve contraction and an even loss of heat throughout the rock.

- **As a lava flow** ceases to move, it begins to cool and form solid igneous rock. The base cools regularly and contraction begins to occur. Cracks develop and columns grow up through the lava.

- **Columnar formations** usually have a more perfect lower part and a less regular shape toward the top.

- **A hexagonal shape** allows the columns to fit together perfectly, but there can be columns with three to eight sides.

43

Rock pillows

- **Rounded masses of lava** called pillow lavas are well-known in the geological record.

- **The Earth's ocean floors** are made of basalt lava with a thin covering of sediment. Fresh basalt lava is continually erupting along the mid-ocean ridges.

- **On the deep seabed**, the composition of basalt lava is changed to form a rock called spilite. This may be because of chemical reactions between the lava and sea water.

- **The "pillow" shape** of the lava masses is caused as a glassy skin cools around each mass of lava. Inside this skin, molten lava continues to move, giving the rounded shape.

- **The lava** may contain gas that enlarges the pillows and also gives the rock a special texture. Gas-bubble holes are left in the lava after the gas has escaped. This is called a vesicular texture.

- **The vesicles** in pillow lavas usually occur in rings that follow the pillow shape. In other lavas, they are randomly situated.

- **On the deep seabed**, pillow lavas are found with other rocks. Often they occur with mudstones.

- **Pillow lava** can also form when basalt erupts into wet mud, or below an ice sheet.

- **The spaces** between the pillows may be filled with broken lava fragments or a rock called chert. This is a very hard, silica-rich material.

- **Pillow lava occurs** in many parts of the world including Britain, south-east Germany, Washington, and North Island, New Zealand.

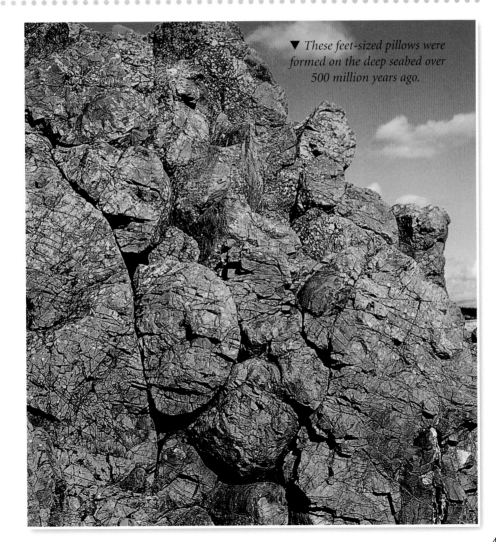

▼ *These feet-sized pillows were formed on the deep seabed over 500 million years ago.*

Geothermal springs

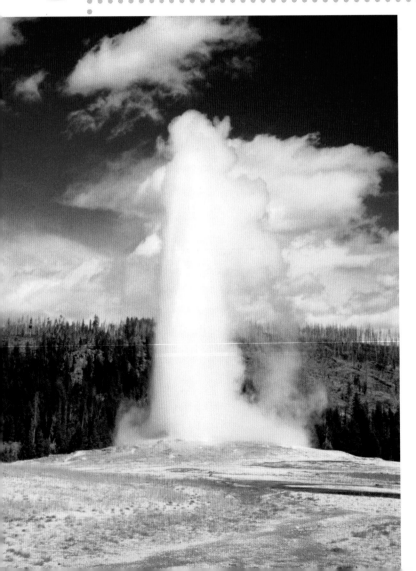

- **In many areas** where volcanic activity takes place (or has recently occurred), there are hot springs, or geysers.

- **The word "geyser"** comes from the Icelandic *geysir*, meaning a "spouter" or "gusher." In Iceland, there are a number of regions where heated underground water gushes to the surface.

◀ *The Old Faithful geyser in Yellowstone National Park, flings steam into the air every hour.*

- **Hot water** from underground is used in Iceland for central heating and heating greenhouses in which fruit, vegetables, and even bananas are grown.

- **In many regions**—such as California, Weiraki, New Zealand, and Larderello, Italy—projects have been established to try to generate electricity from underground steam.

- **An individual geyser** consists of a central pipe with many branches leading from it at depth. Water heated volcanically underground becomes pressurized. As the mass of water boils, it bursts vertically through the central pipe and into the air. Some geysers erupt 230 ft (70 m) into the air.

- **A number of geysers** are very regular in their spouting, and they remain constant over many years.

- **On the surface**, a geyser is surrounded by a pool of silica-rich water at a temperature of about 185°F (85°C). Deposited in this and around its margins is a silica rock called geyserite, which makes a mound around the opening.

- **A fragment of wood** taken from the geyserite surrounding the Old Faithful geyser in Yellowstone National Park, has been dated at 730 years old. This suggests how long that geyser has been spouting.

- **The geyserite** deposited around geysers at Rotorua, New Zealand has built the famous pink and white terraces.

> **...FASCINATING FACT...**
> The Romans appreciated the value of
> hot springs for bathing and laundry.

Uses of igneous rocks

- **Because of their attractive** crystalline surfaces, igneous rocks such as granite and porphyry, are cut and polished for use in buildings. These rocks are frequently found as facings in office blocks, banks, and other commercial buildings.

- **Many granites** and related rocks have large crystals of pink and white feldspar, which give the rocks an attractive appearance.

- **It is currently fashionable** to use "so-called" granite for kitchen work surfaces. The dark-colored igneous rocks used in this way are actually syenites, not granite.

- **The appearance of igneous rocks** is often copied and printed onto other material for use as flooring and surface coverings.

- **Larvikite**, a type of syenite, is especially attractive. It is made of a mass of blue-gray feldspar crystals, which have a distinct silvery sheen.

- **Many igneous rocks** are also very durable. Rocks such as dolerite and basalt, are extensively quarried and then crushed to the required size or grade.

- **Road ballast** is a major use of crushed igneous rock. Half a mile of new road requires 10,000 tons.

- **Aggregate**, often made from finely crushed igneous rock, is used in concrete and building cement. The amount of aggregate required for a new office block may exceed 2,000 tons.

- **As well as being physically strong**, igneous rocks are less susceptible to the effects of acid rain than other rocks, such as limestone.

- **Cemetries** provide examples of different igneous rocks in the form of polished gravestones.

▼ *Granite is often used for buildings as it has an attractive surface made of different mineral crystals and it is relatively resistant to weathering. Tower Bridge, spanning the Thames in London, is partly clad with Cornish granite.*

What are sedimentary rocks?

Sandstone

- **Sedimentary rocks** are best recognized by their layers. These bedding planes, or strata, result from the way the sediment has been deposited.

- **These rocks** are formed in a wide variety of environments on the Earth's surface, and in many cases are easier to study than igneous rocks, which often form at great depth in the Earth's crust.

- **Many sedimentary rocks** are made of particles that have been eroded or weathered from pre-existing rocks. For this reason, they are often referred to as secondary rocks.

- **The particles** are transported by rivers, wind, glaciers, and gravity. During this journey they are changed and may become smaller, more rounded, and broken.

- **Eventually**, when the transporting medium is no longer able to carry the sediment particles, they are deposited. A river, for example, can only carry large pebbles when it is flowing swiftly. As it slows down, so this material is left behind.

- **Most sedimentary rocks** are formed on the seabed. A river entering the sea slows down, depositing its load. The continental shelves have a great thickness of sediment, but much also reaches deeper parts of the oceans.

- **Sedimentary rocks** are of great importance. By looking at their detailed features and comparing these with how modern sediments are being formed, geologists can work out what our past environments were like.

- **Many sedimentary rocks** have great economic significance. Coal was the power behind the Industrial Revolution, and is still an important fuel, used for generating electricity.

- **Our knowledge** of evolution is based on fossil records. Fossils are preserved in sedimentary rocks.

- **Some well-known sedimentary rocks** include sandstone, limestone, mudstone, or shale.

▼ *These high sea cliffs are made of sedimentary sandstone. The strata run almost horizontally.*

Weathering

◀ *Tree roots grow into joints in many rocks. As the roots get larger, the rock is forced apart.*

● **Rocks exposed** on the Earth's surface are broken down in many ways. Weathering causes rock decomposition without involving any movement, or transportation.

● **Weathering** is the first of many processes of denudation (wearing away). These processes result in an overall lowering of the land surface.

● **Many external agents** are involved in weathering, including temperature changes, rain, wind, bacteria, animals, and plants.

● **Weathering** produces the particles of rocks and minerals, which are then transported and deposited as sedimentary rocks.

● **Mechanical weathering** is mainly the result of temperature changes. Water in cracks and joints in rocks expands when it freezes. This creates stresses, which cause rock disintegration. At the base of many mountain slopes and cliffs are scree slopes made of mechanically weathered fragments.

> ... **FASCINATING FACT** ...
> Since the last ice age ended about 10,000 years ago, limestone pavements in North Yorkshire, U.K., have been weathered vertically by 1.5 ft (0.5 m).

◀ *When rocks are heated and cooled in deserts, flakes break off to leave a rounded core.*

● **Temperature changes** can cause the different minerals in a rock to expand and contract at different rates. Stress produced in this way may lead to thin sheets of rock peeling off like the skin of an onion.

● **Chemical weathering** affects many rocks. Limestones are particularly vulnerable. Rainwater is a mild, natural carbonic acid, and with increased acid rain, it becomes more acidic.

● **Limestone** itself is not soluble in rainwater. Calcium carbonate, of which limestones are largely composed, reacts with acid rainwater and soluble calcium bicarbonate is produced.

● **Granite**, often regarded as indestructible, is far from it. The most common mineral in granite is feldspar, which is easily weathered by acid water, especially in tropical conditions. The feldspar rots to clay and the granite is reduced to an incoherent mass of quartz and mica sand.

▶ *In cold climates, water in cracks in the rock turns to ice, forcing the layers apart and fragments are broken off.*

Erosion

▲ *A black moraine of eroded rocks snakes along this glacier surface in Iceland.*

● **Erosion** is the breakdown of rocks and wearing away of the land surface by processes that involve movement.

● **There are many different** environments in which erosion takes place, including rivers, glaciers, seas, and deserts.

● **River erosion** occurs mainly where powerful, rapidly flowing streams cut deep valleys through the landscape. The valley sides are eroded, as is the rock debris carried by the water current. Much eroded sediment is carried to the sea where it is then deposited.

● **The power of river erosion** is well demonstrated by the depth to which the Colorado River has cut its deep V-shaped canyons in Arizona.

● **A glacier** is less fluid than water, and so erodes a deep, reasonably straight valley that has a U-shaped profile. Eroded rock is carried on and within the ice, and deposited when the ice melts.

● **As a glacier moves**, rocks frozen into the ice scrape at the bedrock, eroding marks called striations into it. The ice freezes into cracks in the valley sides and plucks rock fragments away as it moves.

54

> **...FASCINATING FACT...**
> Wind laden with fine sand can strip the
> paint from vehicles in an hour.

- **At the coast**, waves containing sand and pebbles break against cliffs and scour rock pavements. Cliffs are further reduced by landsliding, often assisted by water running over the cliff face or seeping from rocks.

- **In desert regions**, because of the lack of vegetation, the wind is the major erosive factor. Sand picked up by the wind blasts at any upstanding rock masses, concentrating near ground level. Rock pillars are sculpted by this abrasive wind, the weaker strata being eaten away more readily.

- **Larger rock fragments**, which are too heavy to be picked up by the wind, are etched and eroded into three-sided "dreikanter." Such pebbles are well-known from ancient sandstone deposits, and indicate a wind-dominant environment in the distant past.

▼ *Arches National Park. The wind, carrying sand, erodes rocks into amazing shapes.*

How sedimentary rocks are formed

- **Weathering and erosion** provide the particles from which sedimentary rocks are made.

- **Sediments** may form into rocks with no alteration, by a process called lithification. When physical or chemical changes occur during rock formation, the process is called diagenesis.

- **Most sediment** is deposited in the sea. Initially it will be wet and the pore spaces between the grains filled with water. This must be removed to turn the sediment into rock.

- **As layer after layer** of sediment is deposited, the weight and pressure produced begins to affect lower layers. Water may be squeezed out, and the individual grains get packed together more tightly, reducing pore space.

- **When sediment** is first deposited in water, most of it (70–90 percent) is made up of small gaps between the grains. These gaps are called pore spores. As the sediment is buried deeper in the Earth's crust, the pore spores are reduced to only around 30 percent of the rock's volume.

● **In some cases**, where overlying weight is considerable, sand grains may become welded together, with the removal of pore spaces.

● **Many rocks**, like sandstone, do remain porous and may be a valuable source of underground water, gas or oil.

● **Mineral enriched fluids** seep into pore spaces and form natural cements that bind together the individual particles, including pebbles, in sedimentary rocks. A common cement is calcite (calcium carbonate).

● **Quartz** (silicon dioxide) is another common cementing mineral. This hard, chemically resistant cement is common in many sandstones.

● **Limestones** are largely made of calcite, often derived from organic matter. They may be packed with shell fragments, broken crinoid stems, or corals. Recrystallization may occur and the organic material is dissolved, to be replaced by a mosaic of crystalline calcite.

● **Many sediments** undergo color changes as they harden. Iron compounds seeping into pore spaces may color sandstone red or yellow.

◄ *These layers of sand and pebbles may one day become sandstone and breccia.*

57

Environmental evidence

- **Sedimentary rocks** contain evidence that geologists can use to identify the type of environment in which the rock was originally deposited. The rock may have been deposited in the deep ocean, on a beach, glacier, or in a desert.

- **Each environment** leaves behind tell-tale clues in the rock. Geologists need to look at a range of evidence in order to accurately determine the depositional environment of the rocks.

- **The size of the grains** in the rock is a good starting point. On a beach, there are large pebbles, and out in the sea, mud, silt, and sand. Powerful water currents are needed to carry large grains of sediment, and only fine mud can be taken into the deepest oceans.

- **On wet sand**, toward the low tide mark, the sea makes regular patterns called ripple marks. Similar structures are common on sandstone strata, suggesting that these rocks may have been deposited between the tides, by moving river water or by wind in desert environments.

- **A pattern** of joining cracks is made when mud dries out, for example, on the edge of a lake. Such mud-cracks are commonly found on many strata. This suggests these rocks were formed from lake mud.

◀ *This sandstone surface is 150 million years old. It has ripple marks on it that were made on an ancient beach.*

- **Mud cracks** can also indicate arid, desert environments. They can also form on tidal mudflats that dry up. Shrinkage cracks can also form in shallow water (usually sea water).

- **When a large river** flows into the sea, it may deposit a vast delta like that at the mouth of the Mississippi River.

- **There are many** different sedimentary rocks in a delta. Across the delta run many smaller streams, which cut their valleys in the delta sand and mud. Channels carved into sandstones may suggest they originated in a delta.

- **If sandstone strata** are curved and not flat, then the rock may have been formed in a desert as the layers of sand in a dune are gently curved (cross-bedded).

- **Fossils** are often a good clue as to where the sediment was deposited. Some limestones contain fossil corals similar to those found in warm tropical seas today.

◀ *On a modern beach the sea leaves ripple marks on the sand when the tide goes out.*

Sandstone

◀ *The small, rounded quartz grains making this sandstone are clearly seen in this specimen.*

● **Sandstone** is a common sedimentary rock. Essentially, it is made of sand grains compressed together, or cemented by other minerals.

● **Sandstones can be created** in a variety of environments. Some are formed in deserts, some on the seabed, and others in rivers and deltas.

● **Sand grains** blown by the wind tend to be rounded and slightly frosted in appearance. Those carried and deposited by water are usually more angular.

● **The main mineral** in sandstone is quartz. This material is chemically and physically resistant, so is readily able to withstand being transported some distance before being deposited.

● **Some sandstones** contain a relatively high proportion of feldspar. One example is a rock called arkose. Feldspar is easily weathered, so its presence in sandstone suggests that the sediment was deposited quickly.

> ....FASCINATING FACT....
> On the bedding planes of certain sandstones
> small glittery flakes can be seen. These are
> fragments of the mineral called mica.

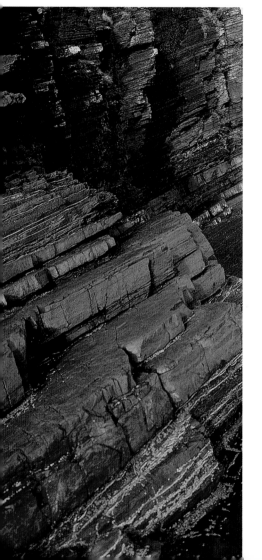

● **Sandstones** generally do not contain as many fossils as other sedimentary rocks such as limestones. However, sandstones formed in the sea can contain mollusk and brachiopod shells, trilobites, and ammonites. Delta sandstones contain plant fossils and some of the best dinosaur fossils are from sandstones formed in river beds and on land.

● **There are many** color varieties of sandstone. These are mainly due to minerals in the rock, some of which cement the sand grains together.

● **Red and yellow** sandstones contain the minerals hematite and limonite around their grains.

● **Sandstones** are economically important. They are used for building as many of them can be cut easily into stones. Porous sandstones can hold water, oil, or gas underground, which can be extracted by means of boreholes.

◄ *The sandstone in these strata are red-colored because of hematite (iron oxide) on the quartz grains.*

Strata and folding

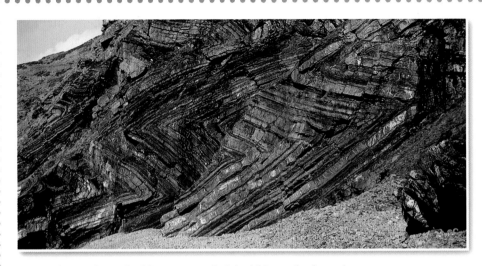

▲ *When rocks are highly compressed, tight folds can be formed.*

- **Many sedimentary rocks** are deposited in neat layers that geologists call strata. Each stratum represents the seabed or land surface at the time it was deposited. The term "bedding planes" is also used for strata.

- **Fossils** may be found on strata. When deposition stops for any length of time, animals and plants may live on the sediment surface, and their remains will be covered over and preserved when deposition resumes.

- **One of the main** principles of geology is that as strata are formed, the oldest one, the first to be deposited, will be at the bottom and the youngest, the most recently formed, will be at the top.

- **If there is continuous** deposition of sediment, then there will be no strata. Sedimentary rocks without strata are said to be massive.

62

- **Strata** can be linked from place to place by using the fossils they contain. The same ammonite fossils found in mudstone in Greenland, shale in Argentina, and limestone in Italy prove that these strata are the same age.

- **The layers of** sedimentary rock were originally deposited horizontally. As the Earth's crust moves, so these layers may be tilted and folded.

- **Though many younger** strata are more or less horizontal, older ones are usually folded. However, the Torridonian sandstones in north-west Scotland are over 900 million years old and have never been folded.

- **Geologists** measure features of folded strata when they make geological maps. The greatest angle that can be measured down a sloping stratum is called the dip of the stratum. This is indicated on a geological map with a small arrow pointing in the direction of the dip and a figure for the angle.

- **When the pressure** is greater from one direction, the folding will be uneven and one side of the fold may even tilt over above the other. This is a recumbent fold. Structures such as these are common in the great mountain ranges such as the Alps and the Andes.

...FASCINATING FACT...
Compression of the crust buckles strata into
upfolds (anticlines) and downfolds (synclines).

Conglomerate and breccia

▶ *Breccia is made of large fragments of sedimentary deposits stuck together.*

● **Conglomerate** is the name geologists give to a sedimentary rock made of large, rounded fragments.

● **Usually**, the pebbles and other fragments are held together with a cement. This may be quartz, calcite, or iron compounds.

● **The pebbles** themselves can be made of many materials. There may be rock fragments that have been eroded and heaped together. Many conglomerates contain pebbles of quartz or quartzite.

● **Conglomerates** are usually deposited near to the area from which their fragments were eroded. Many conglomerates were deposited by rivers. This is because it takes a powerful river current to move such large particles.

● **Many conglomerates** are beach deposits. The fragments will be well-rounded because of being rolled backward and forward by the waves and tide.

● **Some conglomerates** are the deposits of flash floods in predominantly arid areas. Great masses of sand and pebbles lying on the land surface are easily washed along by powerful floods.

- **Breccia** is a rock that is similar to a conglomerate. However, in breccia, the fragments are jagged and angular.

- **Breccia** is deposited very quickly, sometimes without water transportation, so the pebbles and other fragments it contains don't get worn and rounded.

- **Many breccias** are formed as scree by the weathering of high mountain slopes.

- **Rock fragments** are produced when rocks move relatively to each other during faulting. The jumble of broken rock along the fault line is called fault breccia.

▶ *These layers of conglomerate were formed on a river flood plain, when masses of pebbles were carried and deposited by turbulent water, over 200 million years ago.*

Time gaps— unconformities

- **Sedimentary strata** are not deposited continuously. Throughout geological time, there have been considerable gaps in deposition, and often older rocks have been removed by erosion before newer ones have formed.

- **A break** in the geological record is called an unconformity. These are rather puzzling features for a number of reasons.

- **The unconformity** is a rock surface. Below it the rocks may be very different—and much older—than the ones above.

- **Rocks below** an unconformity may be metamorphosed. The rocks above it may be ordinary-looking sedimentary rocks.

- **Geological time** has been recorded for us by events in the rocks. An unconformity represents a break in this record of time.

- **In the far north-west** of Scotland is one of the classic unconformities. The unconformity surface is an old, rough land surface. Below this surface are highly metamorphosed rocks dating back over 2,600 million years. Above the unconformity are stratified sandstones. These are around 900 million years old. This means that 1,700 million years of geological time are not recorded here.

- **Often geologists** can only suggest what might have happened during the time gap at an unconformity. Mountain ranges may have come and gone. Oceans may have flooded the area and disappeared. Sometimes evidence from other, nearby sequences, where more of the rocks have been preserved, can give some clues.

- **Very often**, an unconformity represents a time when much erosion took place. This removed many strata and with them our record of geological time. Then new rocks were deposited on the erosion surface.

- **Rocks** may be folded or tilted before they are eroded. If this occurs there will be a sharp angle between the older rocks and those above the unconformity. This is known as angular unconformity.

- **When the rocks** below and above an unconformity are similar, fossils help geologists to determine the relative age of each set of strata.

▶ *The bottom half of this cliff is made of steeply sloping layers of slate —the top half is limestone. Between the two is an unconformity where the slate was eroded to a flat surface before the deposition of the limestone.*

Manganese nodules

- **In the 1870s**, scientists on the research vessel *Challenger* discovered strange lumps, or nodules, of rock on the beds of the Atlantic and Pacific oceans. As much as 35 percent of the nodules were made up of the metal manganese. The scientists called them manganese nodules.

- **Each nodule** is rather like a potato in size and shape. The outer surface is rough and uneven, and when dry, is dark brown and dusty.

- **Inside**, the nodules are complex. They have an onion-like layering, built up around a grain of sediment or a fossil fragment. It has been proved by radiometric dating that it takes 40 million years for a 4 in (10 cm) nodule to develop.

- **Manganese** is only one of many important metals found in the nodules. They also contain copper, nickel, and cobalt.

- **An extensive survey** of the Pacific Ocean bed was carried out in 1962. This survey found a vast deposit of manganese nodules at a depth of around 16,400 ft (5,000 m).

- **Manganese nodules** are also found in the southern Atlantic Ocean, the Caribbean Sea area, and the southern Indian Ocean.

- **Mining at sea** for the nodules has been carried out by the United States. The ship *Deepsea Miner* dredged the Pacific floor and recovered many tonnes of nodules in the late 1970s.

> **. . . FASCINATING FACT . . .**
> Manganese nodules are a source of metals.
> Manganese and cobalt are used in alloys for the oil
> refining industry. They are also used in jet engines.

- **There are problems** with mining from the deep ocean floor. Even using computerized controls to position the ship, the venture has so far proved very expensive.

- **It is estimated** that 5,500 tons of nodules would have to be recovered every day to make mining worthwhile. The environmental impact of this on deep marine life and the environment would be considerable.

▲ *The curved layers can be seen in this manganese nodule. This specimen was dredged from the seabed 16,400 ft (5,000 m) down in the Pacific Ocean near the Marquesas Islands.*

Deep-sea sediments

▲ *When deep-sea ocean sediments are deposited by turbidity currents, they often result in fine and coarser layers as in these sloping strata. Turbidity currents are rapidly moving masses of sand and mud that flow along the deep seabed.*

- **In the deepest part** of the ocean basins, thousands of miles from land, strange sedimentary deposits accumulate. This region is often referred to as the abyssal part of the oceans.

- **Some sediment** that turns into sedimentary rocks is deposited on the broad continental shelves (the shallow margins around some of the continents).

- **Because the ocean** doesn't have the force to carry sand and pebbles, these are left behind near the shore. Only the finest mud and clay usually travels far out onto the ocean floor. This is carried in suspension in the sea water and only very gradually settles to the seabed. Geologists use the term "ooze" for this dustlike sediment.

- **Icebergs** have been known to float far away from their polar origins. Trapped in these huge blocks of ice is sediment. This can be in the form of clay and sand or giant boulders. Eventually, as the iceberg or ice melts, these are dropped to the deep seabed.

- **Volcanic dust** is often flung high into the atmosphere to circulate in the wind systems. This dust can settle into the oceans and onto the deep seabed.

- **Ocean water** is filled with countless organisms and their skeletons are often made of calcite. These accumulate to make up calcite-rich ooze. This process occurs to a depth of around 13,123 ft (4,000 m). Below this level, on the deepest ocean floors, this deposit is absent. Scientists have discovered that below this depth, calcite is dissolved in the sea water.

- **One unusual type** of sediment found in the deep ocean is made of repeated layers of sand and mud. It has been discovered that these are deposited by rapidly flowing seabed currents, carrying vast amounts of sediment from the land. As the current loses its force, the sand is deposited first and then the mud, giving the alternating layers. Geologists call these currents turbidity currents.

- **In the geological record**, there are thousands of feet of dark, very fine sediment, called mudstone. This rock may contain fossils of planktonic organisms. It is usually regarded as a deep-sea rock.

- **Associated with dark-colored shale**, geologists sometimes find repeated sand layers. These are proof that turbidity currents were at work in the past.

......FASCINATING FACT......
Marine organisms called diatoms and radiolarians
have skeletons made of silica. This material
accumulates on the ocean floor to make silica ooze.

Limestone

▶ *Limestone is often packed with fossils. Those shown here are the remains of water snails.*

- **Limestone** is a sedimentary rock that contains a high proportion of the mineral calcite (calcium carbonate). Often, this is of organic origin.

- **Limestones** are usually pale-colored, being gray, cream, brownish, or buff. Some are very dark and may be almost black because of a high percentage of mud and other eroded sediment.

- **Fossils** are abundant in most limestones. Some of these rocks are named after the fossils they contain. Coral limestone, crinoidal, and shelly limestone are rich in these fossils. Limestone may be a mass of fossils cemented together by calcite.

- **Most limestone deposits** are geologically young. Organisms that developed hard calcite shells, from which the rock is often made, didn't evolve until Cambrian times. Pre-cambrian limestone is often made of calcite secreted by colonies of blue-green algae, forming mounds called stromatolites.

- **Chemical weathering** easily attacks limestone. The rock is etched into characteristic structures, and joints are enlarged as water runs through them. Underground cave and stream systems develop, and there is often a complete lack of surface drainage.

- **Dolostone** (dolomite) is a type of limestone in which much of the calcite has been changed into the mineral dolomite. Dolomite is a double carbonate of calcium and magnesium. It forms as the rock hardens.

- **Oolitic limestone** is made of small, rounded grains (ooliths) of sediment. These are of chemical origin and made of concentric layers of calcite. The layers are formed around a small shell fragment or sand grain. Today, oolitic limestones are forming around the Bahama Banks in the Caribbean.

- **Reef limestones** are fossilized sediment reefs. They contain a variety of fossils of organisms that live in the shallow reef environment. These may include corals, trilobites, brachiopods, mollusks, and crinoids.

- **The reef** itself is a mound of sediment, the surface of which is near to sea level. Some reefs may be composed of a lime mud, secreted by various micro-organisms.

- **Limestone** has many important economic uses and is often extensively quarried. For many years it has been powdered for agricultural purposes. Limestone is an important building stone and forms the basis of cement.

◀ *Limestone landscapes often have much bare rock. This is because there is very little surface water so soil doesn't form and plants cannot grow.*

73

Chalk

- **Chalk** is a special type of limestone. It is almost pure white, very fine grained, and most contains over 90 percent calcium carbonate (calcite).

- **Chalk** is a sedimentary rock that was deposited in the sea, probably away from the continental shelf, in regions where there was little seabed disturbance.

- **Most chalk** occurs in western Europe and in some parts of North America, for example in the state of Kansas. European chalk was deposited during the Cretaceous Period between 142 and 65 million years ago.

- **The famous white cliffs** along the south coast of England, which for years have been a landmark for travelers, are composed of chalk.

- **One of the puzzles** about chalk is its great purity. There is an almost complete lack of sand or mud and other sediment carried from the land.

- **Much of the nearest land** was probably very low lying, without hills and mountains. Because of this there would have been very little erosion bringing mud or sand into the sea.

- **Virtually all the calcite** in chalk is the remains of small organisms. These include microscopic creatures called coccoliths.

- **Large fossils** are found in chalk. These include ammonites and other mollusks, brachiopods, and echinoids (sea urchins).

◀ *Chalk is a white powdery rock made of the remains of minute sea creatures.*

▲ *Along the south coast of England there are many high chalk cliffs, as shown here at Bat's Head in Dorset.*

● **The layers of chalk** are divided into time zones using ammonite fossils.

● **A variety of creatures** lived in and on the soft seabed. Worms and sea urchins burrowed into the chalky mud. Sponges and mollusks also lived on the seabed.

Flint

▶ *When carefully chipped, flint can be used to make tools such as this pointed hand ax.*

- **Flint** is a hard, nodular rock, found in irregular layers in chalk.

- **Flints** can be seen in chalk cliffs as dark parallel bands running among the white strata.

- **Like the common mineral quartz**, flint is composed of silicon dioxide. Quartz usually forms hexagonal crystals but flint is different. The crystals making up flint are so small that a powerful microscope is needed to see them.

- **The silica** in flint is derived from small sea creatures. It mainly comes from the internal supports of sponges. It is believed that concentrations of silica formed within the chalk sediment and hardened into flint.

- **Large fossils** are sometimes replaced by flint, such as the heartshaped sea urchin called *Micraster*.

- **"False flints"** are hollow inside. Here the silica formed around a sponge, that eventually disintegrated, leaving a hollow. These false flints have a white powdery interior made from the shells of single-celled foraminferans and ostracods (creatures related to water fleas).

- **When flint** is seen on the surface of a chalk stratum, the nodular lumps may occur in rings.

- **Flint** is so hard that it cannot be scratched with a knife blade. It breaks easily into curved shapes with very sharp edges.

- **The durability and sharpness** of broken flint has been exploited in the past.

- **Early man** used flints to make hand axes from at least 2 million years ago. These were shaped by chipping flakes of flint from around a core, using a hammer stone. Flint has continued to be used in tools right up until the early 1800s when flintlocks were still being made.

▶ *Flint is often dark-colored and breaks with sharp jagged edges. It is a very pure type of silicon dioxide.*

Ice age rocks

- **The most recent ice age** ended in Britain and most of Europe and North America around 10,000 years ago. Much evidence for this ice age can be found in the landforms created by the ice sheets and glaciers and in their special sedimentary rocks.

- **Glacial rocks** are known from much older times. There is evidence of an ice age that affected parts of Scotland in the Permian Era. Glacial sediments occur in Brazil that were formed during the Carboniferous and Permian Periods (355–250 million years ago). These are 5,250 ft (1600 m) thick in places, suggesting an amazing amount of erosion by the ancient glaciers.

- **As glaciers and ice sheets** move, they pick up fresh and eroded rock material. This is carried in, on, and beneath the ice. Eventually, as the ice melts, deposition occurs.

- **A typical feature** of many glacial sedimentary rocks is that they are badly sorted. This means that within one deposit there will be fragments of many sizes, from fine clay to large boulders.

- **Glacial rocks** are commonly un-bedded. They do not have the neat strata that identify most sedimentary rocks.

- **The term moraine** is used to cover a wide variety of glacial deposits. It may consist of sand, gravel, clay, and rock fragments. Much eroded rock debris falls along the sides of a glacier. This lateral moraine may be further eroded against the valley sides as the ice moves.

- **A push moraine** is bulldozed along at the glacier snout (front end). Any glacier may produce a number of these as it retreats and then re-advances. Terminal moraines usually form in this way, and give geologists evidence about the furthest position a glacier reached.

- **If two valley glaciers** join, their lateral moraines will merge to form a medial moraine in the new, larger glacier.

- **Much meltwater** is associated with glaciers. This flows out from under the ice carrying sediment. Usually meltwater is thick and milky-looking because of the clay it contains. The area in front of the glacier snout is called an outwash plain. Water-formed sediments occur here, often in neat strata.

- **The large boulders** (and other rocks) carried and dumped by the ice are often left stranded and out of place. These are called erratics, and their significance is considerable. By studying the erratics, geologists are able to tell from where a long-vanished ice sheet came.

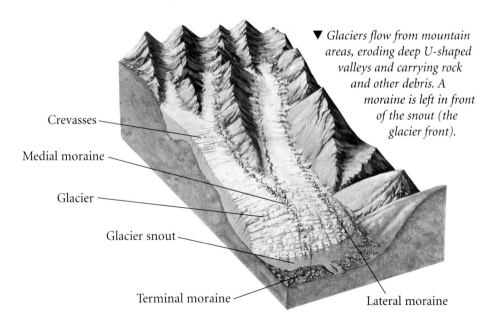

▼ *Glaciers flow from mountain areas, eroding deep U-shaped valleys and carrying rock and other debris. A moraine is left in front of the snout (the glacier front).*

Crevasses

Medial moraine

Glacier

Glacier snout

Terminal moraine

Lateral moraine

Coal

- **Coal** is the classic fossil fuel that provided power to the 19th century Industrial Revolution. It is the most abundant and easiest fossil fuel to recover.

- **Coal is the consolidated remains** of carbon stored in plants. These plants, living hundreds of millions of years ago, took in energy from sunlight and stored it in their tissues. When a light bulb is switched on, using electricity generated in a coal-fired power station, "fossil sunlight" is being released.

- **Coal** is most common in strata of the Carboniferous Period (355–298 million years ago). It is found in rocks from the Permian Period (298–250 million years ago), in South Africa, Brazil, China, and Australia and in rocks from the Triassic Period (250–208 million years ago) in China and eastern U.S.A.

- **Coal from** the Jurassic Period (208–144 million years ago) has been mined in England, northeast Scotland, Siberia, and China. Rocks containing coal from the Cretaceous Period (144–65 million years ago) occur in Siberia, northern Germany, and Canada.

- **The coal-forming plants** of the Carboniferous Period developed from peat deposited in the sedimentary layers of sand and mud formed on a vast delta.

- **Peat** is the first stage in the development of coal. This is a brown, often very waterlogged, material which has formed from partially decayed plant matter. For peat to be a useful fuel it has to be cut into blocks and dried.

...FASCINATING FACT...
At the present rate of use, coal will long
outlast oil and gas as a fossil fuel resource.

- **In some parts of the world**, peat is used for domestic heating. It is burned in power stations in some countries, such as Ireland.

- **As peat is buried** under more accumulated sediment, it becomes compressed and heated. The increase in temperature drives off impurities, including water. Gradually, the percentage of carbon in the peat increases, and it becomes (brown) lignite and then coal.

- **Bituminous coal** contains a far higher percentage of carbon than lignite and is the most widely used coal, but produces much ash.

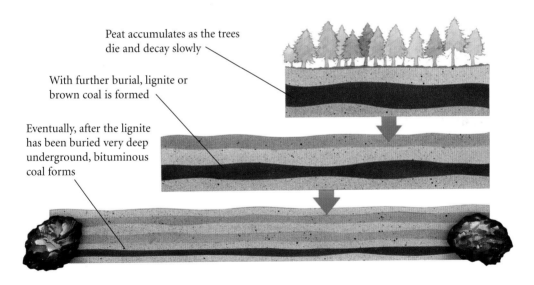

Peat accumulates as the trees die and decay slowly

With further burial, lignite or brown coal is formed

Eventually, after the lignite has been buried very deep underground, bituminous coal forms

▲ *Most coal was formed from trees and other vegetation living in swampy conditions. The dead trees formed peat as they rotted very slowly and eventually after being buried and heated under thousands of feet of rock, the peat turned to coal.*

81

Oil and gas

- **Oil and gas** are fossil fuels. Natural gas, commonly found with oil, has in many places taken over from coal gas as an important domestic and industrial fuel.

- **Oil** has given wealth to many nations that otherwise were poor.

- **Oil is a mixture** of many different hydrocarbons (compounds made largely of hydrogen and carbon) derived from marine organisms.

- **Oil and gas** are very mobile and move, under pressure, through strata, away from where they were formed.

- **Usually**, oil and gas are 'trapped' below ground. They move upward through porous or permeable strata. Limestone and sandstone are good at allowing this movement. Eventually the moving fluids may come to a non-porous layer such as mudstone. Their movement is halted. The oil and gas then accumulate in the porous strata below the cap rock in an oil "trap". The strata containing oil often lie on top of strata containing brine (highly salted water) and gas occurs above the oil-rich layer.

▶ *Significant reserves of oil and gas have been discovered in the rock under the seabed. The fossil fuel is obtained using oil rigs—large platforms anchored to the seabed.*

- **Oil and gas** may eventually leak out onto the Earth's surface. When this happens, no geological exploration and surveying is needed to find the fossil fuels.

- **Oil does not always flow up** to the surface, and in many oilfields it has to be pumped to the surface by machines called "nodding donkey."

▲ *A "nodding donkey" pumping oil from Jurassic strata.*

- **When geologists** go out prospecting for oil, they look for structures where oil may be trapped. Areas where there is little soil and vegetation can be photographed from the air and structures show up readily. On the ground, porous strata can be detected below the surface by measuring the electrical resistance of rocks or their reaction to shock waves from small explosions.

- **Most oil** is discovered by drilling boreholes. Drilling for oil requires a lubricant called drilling mud. This keeps the drill bit cool. It is commonly made of heavy minerals and volcanic clay.

- **In some areas** such as the North Sea, oil was not found in the areas first prospected. Gas was present, however, and this became an important resource in the 1960s.

Evaporite rocks

- **The term "evaporite"** is used for a range of rocks deposited from salt water. Rock salt (halite), rock gypsum, and potash are the three most common and economically important evaporite rocks. Geologists classify all these deposits as chemical rocks.

- **The main evaporite deposits** exploited for their chemicals are formed from minerals in sea water.

- **If part of the sea**, such as a bay or gulf, is cut off from the open ocean by a sand bank, it will begin to dry up, especially in a hot, dry climate. This is the start of evaporite formation.

- **Some evaporite deposits** occur where inland salt lakes have dried out.

- **In the sea**, a series of evaporite rocks is deposited in a definite sequence. The rocks are usually interbedded with mudstone, which contains a high amount of calcite (calcium carbonate).

- **Some of the evaporite chemicals** are more soluble in water than others. The least soluble form layers of rock first. The most soluble remain in solution until the water has virtually dried out. The first to occur as strata are often gypsum and anhydrite. Rock salt is the next to form, and finally a mixture of potash rocks.

- **Many evaporite deposits** are forming at the present time, especially in arid regions. These are usually processed where they occur.

- **Of the marine evaporates**, rock salt (halite) is essential for human and animal health. It has been in great demand for thousands of years as a food enhancer and preserver. Gypsum and anhydrite are used for making sulphuric acid and fertilizers and for plaster and plasterboard. Potash is used as the basis of agricultural fertilizers.

84

- **The evaporites** deposited in land-bound lakes include borax and nitrates. Borax is used in glass, paper, and leather products. Nitrates are the basis of fertilizers, explosives, and nitric acid.

- **In Britain** there are considerable evaporite (halite) deposits in Cheshire and also in North Yorkshire, where mines over 3 mi (5 km) deep go out under the North Sea. Other important deposits occur in Germany, the U.S.A., and Chile.

▼ *Potash is used on a large scale for making agricultural fertilizers. This mine, in the North York Moors National Park, U.K. is over 3 mi (5 km) deep and tunnels stretch out below the nearby seabed.*

Stalactites and stalagmites

- **The roofs** of many limestone caves are covered with hanging, icicle-shaped growths made of calcium carbonate. These are called stalactites. The structures growing on the cave floor are stalagmites.

- **Limestone**, which is a common sedimentary rock, is easily weathered by chemical processes. Acid rainwater changes the calcite in limestone into soluble calcium bicarbonate, which is carried away.

▼ *Straw stalactites develop where water rich in calcium bicarbonate seeps through many small openings in a cave roof.*

> **...FASCINATING FACT...**
> In western Ireland, a stalactite has been
> found that is 20.7 ft (6.3 m) long.

- **Chemical weathering** of limestone along bedding planes and joints allows water to run underground. Passages are eroded by this water, and as they grow in size, cave systems develop.

- **In the British Isles**, limestone caves have been formed in north-west Scotland, Derbyshire, North Yorkshire, Gloucestershire, Devon, and western Ireland.

- **The opening** on the surface down which water runs is called a pot hole. Gaping Gill pothole in North Yorkshire is 394 ft (120 m) deep.

- **Water dripping** from a limestone cave roof is full of dissolved calcium bicarbonate. This is deposited as calcium carbonate (calcite) as the water drips into the cave and in part evaporates. The calcite is deposited in concentric rings to form stalactites.

- **Stalagmites** usually form beneath a stalactite from water dripping off its tip. They are more stumpy and shorter.

- **Stalactites**, hanging from the cave roof tend to be slender. Some, known as straw stalactites, are very small, but some are huge and can grow to many feet in length.

- **Both structures** are made of many layers of calcite. If cut open, the concentric rings of calcite can be seen. Sometimes, a stalactite and a stalagmite will join together to form a column.

Superposition

- **Geology,** like any science, has a number of laws, or principles, which help scientists to interpret rocks. The principle of superposition is one of these.

- **William Smith** (1769–1839), an English canal engineer and pioneering geologist, established the principle of superposition.

- **In simple terms**, the law of superposition states that in a sequence of sedimentary rocks, the older rocks lie below the younger layers.

- **A geologist** in the field may have problems interpreting strata according to this principle. In extreme conditions, folding, for example, will overturn the beds of rock so that younger layers lie beneath older ones.

- **Similarly a "thrust fault"** may force old rocks above younger ones, which is another reason why the principle cannot be applied.

- **There are a number** of ways in which a geologist can prove if rocks are the correct "way up." These need to be applied before the order of strata can be determined.

- **Each stratum** marks a break in the deposition of sediment. On its surface various marks may be made. These prove which way up it formed. The sediment may be rippled, like a modern beach. If sediment dried out, mud cracks would be formed.

- **Fossils of animals** such as mollusk shells in their burrows, can also be used to show whether the rocks are the correct way up.

- **Volcanic rocks** that contained much gas will have their vesicles (gas-bubble holes) at the top of a lava flow.

▶ *On this wave-cut platform, the older strata are closer to the sea and youngest ones on the land. Each stratum dips (slopes) toward the land and disappears below a younger (higher) layer.*

Ironstones

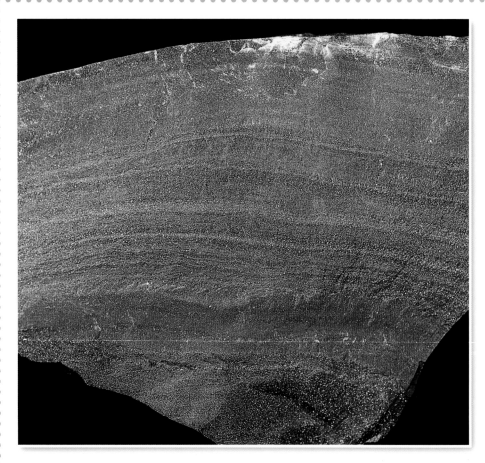

▲ *Banded ironstone is one of the richest ores of iron. This example comes from Western Australia.*

- **At least 90 percent** of all the iron mined and quarried each year is in the form of the sedimentary rock called ironstone.

- **Ironstones** formed in shallow water in the sea, near to land.

- **Iron** is one of the most sought after metals. It is used in the manufacture of steel, the main uses of which are in building and vehicle production.

- **The presence of iron** compounds in sedimentary rocks colors them red or yellowish-brown.

- **Some types of iron** are soluble in water and are carried to areas where sedimentary rocks are being deposited.

- **Iron** is easily oxidized (rusted) so is not very stable in today's climate. In the Precambrian Era (more than 600 million years ago), there was very little oxygen in the atmosphere, as there were no true land plants. Iron compounds were more stable at this time.

- **Very old rocks** of Precambrian age, which are rich in iron, occur in the U.S.A. around Lake Superior, Labrador in Canada, the Ukraine, Western Australia, and Brazil.

- **Precambrian ironstones** are called banded ironstones because of their structure. They have thin, alternating layers of chert (a form of silicon dioxide) and iron oxide. These ores may contain up to 65 percent iron.

- **The ironstones** on which heavy industry was founded during the 19th century are of relatively low iron content—often less than 30 percent iron.

- **Many ironstones** have an oolitic structure, being made of small, rounded grains coated with iron minerals.

Rocks in the home

- **Slate,** a metamorphic rock that splits easily into thin slabs, is used for roofing in many parts of the world.

- **The walls** of buildings have been made of local stone of various kinds for thousands of years. The most suitable stones to use are 'freestones', which can be easily cut in any direction.

- **Attractive,** polished stones such as granite, syenite, marble, and limestone are often used for mantlepieces and other decorative features such as facing stones.

- **Chimneys** may have liners made from clay to allow a smoother passage for smoke and reduce the risk of heat damage to stone or brick work.

- **Coal** is still used in many areas as a source of heating in the home. Electric power is largely generated by using this fossil fuel.

- **Plaster and plasterboard,** which are used to build interior walls, are made from the rock gypsum.

- **Cement,** which binds bricks, is made of limestone and mudstone.

- **Rock salt** is important as a flavouring for food. It is used in cooking, served as a condiment and is also used to preserve meat, fish and other foods.

- **The volcanic rock** pumice, is used for rubbing away dead skin.

- **Many kitchens** have a pestle and mortar for grinding food and spices. These are made from a variety of different rocks, including marble, granite, and syenite.

- **Bricks** are made from a wide variety of mudstones, quarried thoughout the U.K.

▼ *Pool and snooker tables of high quality have their beds made of slate. This metamorphic rock can be split into perfectly flat layers and it doesn't warp when temperature or humidity changes.*

Aquifers

● **Many rocks**, such as sandstone and limestone, are porous. There are spaces or pores between the grains making up the rock, or there are joints, fissures, and cavities that can all hold water.

● **Rocks** may also be permeable. These have joints and other cracks running through them that allow water to move underground.

● **An aquifer** is any rock that can retain or carry water and allow water to move through it. Aquifers are often very important sources of domestic and industrial water supply.

● **Water** held in an aquifer may sometimes flow out onto the surface.

● **The water table** is the level below which there is permanent saturation. It is not always the same level, and will depend on rainfall and river run-off.

● **Underground auifers** supply 25–30 percent of the water supply in England and Wales.

◀ *The limestone strata in these cliffs are permeable and allow water to run through and be held underground. When there is excess rainfall, the underground water level rises and springs form along a layer of impermeable rock near the foot of the cliffs.*

- **London** has a natural aquifer in the form of a syncline (downfold) of porous chalk. This structure forms the Chiltern Hills in the north, then dips below the capital and emerges as the North Downs to the south.

- **To obtain water** from an aquifer, boreholes are sunk. The water flows under pressure through these to the surface. Natural flow to the surface is called artesian flow.

- **Much of London's** water supply comes from a natural aquifer of chalk dipping below the capital city.

- **The sandstones** that date back to the Triassic Period, underlying Cheshire and Lancashire in the U.K., form an aquifer in areas of heavy industry and high population.

◀ In the past, the pressure in London's aquifer was enough to supply the fountains in Trafalgar Square.

95

Deltas

- **A delta** is a mass of sediment built up at the mouth of a river where it enters a lake or the sea.

- **The Mississippi Delta** in the Gulf of Mexico, has built up "fingers" of low-lying land. Here, there is little tide or wave energy to move the sediment.

- **Sediment** is deposited when a river enters deep water because its speed and power to transport sediment suddenly decreases.

- **Deltaic rocks** include mudstones and sandstones. Coal seams may be found in sequences of deltaic rocks.

  - **Because the top** of a delta is very close to sea level, a very slight increase in the sea level will cause flooding.

    - **Millions of people** live and work on the Ganges and Brahmaputra delta region of north-east India and Bangladesh. Monsoon rains and storms in the Bay of Bengal often inundate the low-lying delta, with devastating results.

◀ *The Nile delta has many distributary channels, between which are low-lying areas of fertile river sediment called alluvium.*

...FASCINATING FACT...
Around 320 million years ago, much of Britain was submerged beneath a vast delta.

- **Many major oilfields** are in ancient delta rocks. These include the oilfields of Nigeria, the southern U.S.A., and the North Sea.

- **The building** of the Aswan Dam in Egypt has prevented sediment entering the Nile delta.

- **The marsh and water habitats** found on many deltas are home to a great variety of wildlife.

▲ *This sandstone was formed in a delta over 270 million years ago. The V-shaped mass of sandstone in the top half of the picture is the cross-section of a stream bed, which flowed across the delta, filled with sandstone.*

Desert rocks

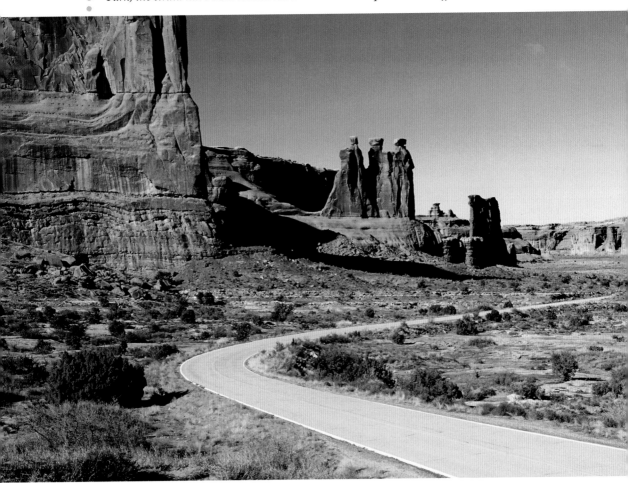

▼ *Rocks formed in arid areas are often red or orange colored. Here, in the Arches National Park, the strata have been weathered and eroded into pillars and cliffs.*

- **Deserts** are arid regions that receive very low rainfall, usually not enough to support vegetation.

- **Most desert regions** are areas of high temperatures, but Antarctica is also a desert.

- **By studying** the sediments and other features of today's deserts, geologists can work out which rocks were formed in ancient deserts.

- **Sandstone** is one of the main desert rocks. The grains are rounded by wind action.

- **The strata** formed by the wind are not horizontal. Instead, curved "cross-bedded" layers are formed.

- **Larger fragments** of quartz are often pitted and frosted by sand blasting.

- **Deserts are very windy** environments, so mica, a mineral that occurs in small flakes, is absent from desert rocks.

- **If rain does** fall on a desert region, it is usually very heavy for a short time. This creates flash floods, which can carry sand, pebbles, and boulders.

- **"Desert rose"** is a flower-like formation of the mineral gypsum that forms in deserts.

> ...FASCINATING FACT...
> Many desert rocks are red-colored because
> they contain iron oxide.

Concretions and nodules

- **Concretions and nodules** are rounded masses of rock found in many sedimentary rocks. They commonly occur in rows following the strata.

- **Most concretions** are a few inches in diameter, but some are measured in feet.

- **When they occur** in mudstone, concretions may be made of pyrite (iron sulphide), iron (siderite), calcite, or phosphate.

- **Sandstone** often contains concretions that may be rich in iron compounds.

- **Flint forms** as nodules in the Cretaceous chalk. These dark masses are easily seen against the white rock.

- **Concretions** are often made of the same material in which they occur. They probably form after the sediment has been deposited, as it is turning to rock.

▼ *These rounded nodules in a Jurassic shale cliff are about 8 in (20 cm) across. Often nodules such as these follow a particular stratum.*

▲ *These cracks have formed in a concretion as it has shrunk after formation. They are filled in with the mineral calcite.*

- **In some strata**, especially the lower Jurassic mudstones, concretions can contain well-preserved fossils. These are mainly mollusks such as ammonites.

- **A septarian nodule,** or concretion, is filled with radiating or concentric veins of mineral, often calcite. The veins occupy shrinkage cracks created as the nodules dry out.

- **Concretions and nodules** are usually more resistant to erosion than the mudstone in which they often occur.

101

Metamorphic rocks

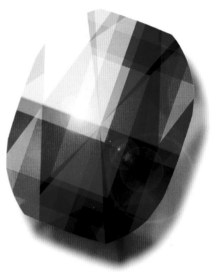

▶ *Garnet is a mineral that forms in many metamorphic rocks, especially schist. It is used as a semi-precious gemstone and may be cut and facetted.*

- **Metamorphic rocks** are any rocks that have been changed by heat, pressure, or a combination of these forces.

- **Most metamorphic changes** occur at temperatures of between 392°F–1,292°F (200°C–700°C). The extreme pressure at which rocks metamorphose is up to 6,000 times greater than atmospheric pressure and can occur at a depth of 12.4 mi (20 km).

- **Contact metamorphism** involves only heat. Regional metamorphism is brought about by heat and pressure.

- **No melting of rock** occurs during metamorphism. When melting takes place, magma, from which igneous rocks are formed, is created.

- **The chemical composition** and structure of a rock can be changed by metamorphism.

- **When large-scale faulting** occurs, dislocation metamorphism takes place.

- **Original structures**, such as strata in sedimentary rocks, are removed during metamorphism.

▶ *Where rocks are highly folded deep underground, they are altered by regional metamorphism. Rocks near to magma are changed by contact metamorphism.*

Strata near to magma are changed by contact metamorphism

Layers of rock away from the heat remain unchanged

Rock can become folded and regionally metamorphosed

- **Fossils are sometimes found** in slightly metamorphosed rocks such as slate. As the degree of metamorphism increases, fossils are destroyed.

- **Garnet**, a mineral much used as a semi-precious gemstone, is common in the metamorphic rock called schist.

- **Some of the oldest rocks** in the Earth's crust are highly metamorphosed gneisses.

103

Contact metamorphism

- **Contact metamorphism** occurs when rocks are heated by magma or lava.

- **A metamorphic aureole** is the region around a mass of magma in which rocks have been altered.

- **A lava flow** can only metamorphose the rocks lying below it.

- **The amount** of contact metamorphism depends on the size of the igneous body producing heat and any fluids seeping from it.

- **The metamorphic aureole** around a large batholith may be a few miles wide.

- **A small sill**, dyke or lava flow may metamorphose rocks up to only a few inches away.

- **A gradual** metamorphic change takes place away from the igneous intrusion. The rocks furthest away are only slightly metamorphosed. Right next to the intrusion they may be highly altered.

- **Dark-colored "spots"** and clusters of minerals are a common feature of clay and shale that have been altered by contact metamorphism. With great heat, a tough rock called hornfels is formed.

- **When heated**, limestone becomes crystalline marble. This new rock is a mosaic of calcite crystals, often with veins of green or blue minerals.

- **Sandstone** is changed to a hard, crystalline rock called metaquartzite.

▶ *The sloping rock surface on the right is made of granite. When it formed deep underground nearly 300 million years ago, intense heat from the magma metamorphosed the dark hornfels on the left of the picture.*

Marble

- **Marble** is formed by the contact metamorphism of limestone.

- **Heat** from an igneous intrusion or lava flow causes the calcite in the limestone to recrystallize.

- **Original features** in the limestone, such as strata and fossils, are destroyed, and an interlocking mosaic of calcite crystals forms.

- **Pure limestones** become very pale, often sugary, marbles, with very little color veining.

- **Limestone**, that has impurities in the form of clay, other sedimentary material, and minerals are changed into colorfully veined marbles.

- **The metamorphic minerals** brucite, olivine, and serpentine can give marble a greenish coloring.

- **Olivine marble** has small patches of bright green or brown olivine. This is a silicate mineral formed by the heat of metamorphism.

- **For over 2,500 years**, marble has been prized as a decorative stone. This is because it is easily shaped and polished, and has attractive coloring.

▶ *The abandoned marble quarry on the Isle of Iona, western Scotland. Marble was quarried here and much was shipped to Europe. This quarry closed in 1914.*

- **In the classical Greek** and Roman periods, marble was the main rock used for statues.

- **Michelangelo's *David*,** carved between 1501 and 1504, is one of the most well-known marble statues in existence.

Metaquartzite

- **When sandstone** is altered by contact metamorphism, it turns into metaquartzite.

- **Heat from** an igneous intrusion or lava flow causes the quartz grains in sandstone to grow and fuse together.

- **Metaquartzite** may have only faint traces of the original bedding, and any fossils in the original sandstone will have been destroyed.

- **Sandstone** is more resistant to metamorphic change than many other rocks because so much heat is needed to alter it.

- **Metaquartzite** is a pale-colored rock, often with a sugary texture.

- **Sandstone** is a porous rock with small spaces between the grains. Metaquartzite is crystalline and non-porous.

- **Because it is largely made** of quartz, metaquartzite is a very hard rock. It is resistant to weathering.

▶ *Originally sandstone, this metaquartzite is now a mosaic of quartz crystals. The original layers in the rock have disappeared.*

- **Metaquartzite is quarried** and used in the construction industry.

- **Metaquartzite is found** very close to large batholiths. Smaller intrusions rarely have sufficient heat to change quartz-rich sandstone.

- **Though it is virtually 100 percent quartz,** metaquartzite may contain feldspar and iron oxides in small amounts.

▶ *The pale-colored metaquartzite in this cliff still has some of its original features—strata are visible.*

Crushed rock

- **Large-scale faulting** causes rocks along the fault surface to be crushed and metamorphosed.

- **Fault breccia** is a rock made of angular broken fragments. It is common along many fault lines.

- **The crushed rock** formed when thrust faults move deep in the Earth's crust is called mylonite.

- **Mylonite** is made from the dusty rock "flour" that is created as rocks are ground up along the fault plane. Larger fragments, often stretched out, are stuck into this.

- **If thrust faults** occur deep in the crust where temperatures are high, new minerals will grow in mylonite. Chlorite, mica, feldspar, and epidote are common examples.

- **As the fault moves**, rock flour and minerals are stretched out to give mylonite its typical texture.

- **Mylonite tends to break** in thin plates and slabs parallel to its texture.

▲ *Mylonite seen very close-up shows minerals streaked out during its formation. The pale mineral here is quartz.*

- **Geologists** use the term "cataclasis" for the processes that create mylonite.
- **Large-scale thrust faults** occur in areas of mountain building.
- **There are a number** of thrust faults, with associated mylonite, in the north-west Highlands of Scotland.

▼ *The Glencoul thrust fault, Sutherland, Scotland. The thrust plane is the sloping surface halfway up the hillside. The grey mass of rock above it has moved from the right along the thrust plane above younger rocks.*

Faulting

- **Faults** are breaks in the rocks of the Earth's crust where the rocks move relative to each other. The same stratum will be at a different level on each side of the fault.

- **A joint** is a break in the rocks where no movement takes place.

- **Both faults and joints** are often the places where hot, mineral-rich fluids rise through the crust. Important mineral reserves occur in this way.

- **The actual surface** where the rocks break and move is called the fault plane. In many faults, such as normal and reversed faults, the fault plane is very steep. Thrust faults have a fault plane sloping at only a few degrees.

- **When faults move**, earthquakes occur. Movement on the San Andreas Fault that runs through California, threatens large cities such as Los Angeles.

- **A normal fault** is where the Earth's crust stretches and one mass of rock moves down a break—the fault plane.

- **If two normal faults** occur parallel to each other a block of the crust may sink between them. This is called a rift, or graben. The region of rift valleys in east Africa was formed in this way.

- **Where a reverse fault** occurs, the Earth's crust is made thicker by compression. One mass of rock is forced up the fault plane relative to the rocks on the other side.

- **In a tear fault**, there is virtually no vertical movement. Rock masses are moved sideways relative to each other.

> ...FASCINATING FACT...
> A thrust fault can move huge masses of rock many tens
> of miles up a very low angled fault plane.

▼ *Unlike most faults, the San Andreas Fault in California is visible on the Earth's surface.*

Regional metamorphism

- **As the name implies**, this type of metamorphism occurs over great areas of the Earth's crust.

- **Regional metamorphism** happens when mountain building, often associated with movement of the Earth's lithospheric plates, occurs.

- **Pressure and heat** are involved in altering rocks by regional metamorphism.

- **The changes** that take place during regional metamorphism may take tens of millions of years to occur.

Gneiss

- **Some of the oldest rocks** in the Earth's crust have been affected by regional metamorphism. These have been radiometrically dated at over 3,500 million years old.

- **The deeper** into the crust that rocks are taken by the processes of mountain building, the higher the degree, or grade, of metamorphism they suffer.

- **Rocks** formed by regional metamorphism are identified by their texture. Because of stresses in the rock, minerals are streaked out in layers.

- **High-grade rocks**—those that are altered most—are called gneiss. With increased temperature, caused by depth of burial, melting may occur and magma is created.

- **At lower depths**, where the temperature and pressure are lower, a rock called schist is formed.

114

● **Around the margins** of the mountain region, temperatures are very low. Here, pressure is also low and rocks such as slate are created.

▼ *Regional metamorphism occurs in the roots of mountain chains. Deep below the Alps in Switzerland, slate, schist, and gneiss are forming.*

115

Slate

- **Slate** forms around the margins of mountain regions where the lowest grade of regional metamorphism occurs.

- **Slates** are dark-colored rocks made of grains and crystals too small to be seen with the naked eye.

- **The most recognizable feature** of slate is its cleavage. This is the way the rock splits into thin, neat layers. However, the most weakly metamorphosed slates may not have developed a cleavage.

- **Because it splits** so easily, slate has been used for hundreds of years for roofing and gravestones.

- **Fossils** may still be present in slate. These are often squashed or stretched by the stresses that metamorphosed the rock.

- **Slate** forms from the weak metamorphism of mudstone or siltstone.

- **Small, golden-colored crystals** of pyrite (fool's gold) form in some slates.

- **Green slate** is colored by the mineral chlorite, which grows under metamorphic stress.

- **Some of the world's** most important slate quarries are in North Wales, U.K. Slate from there has been shipped all over the world.

- **Slate** is also found in other parts of Britain, including Cumbria, Scotland and Devon. Elsewhere in the world, it occurs in California, Onijarvi, Finland, and Vosges, France.

▶ *This specimen of slate contains crystals of pyrite (iron sulphide). Pyrite often forms during regional metamorphism. The rock has broken along a cleavage surface.*

Schist

- **Schist** forms at higher temperatures and pressures than slate. These conditions occur deeper in the Earth's crust and nearer the center of a mountain region.

- **Schist** is a silvery rock because it contains mica—this may be pale muscovite or dark biotite mica.

- **A typical feature** of schist is a wavy banding (called schistosity) running through the rock. This results from the way minerals have lined up during metamorphism.

- **As well as mica**, this rock contains quartz and feldspar.

- **Many new minerals** can form in schist during metamorphism. These include garnet, kyanite, hornblende, and epidote.

- **Because temperatures** and pressure are moderately high when schists form, most rocks are altered.

- **Garnet schists** are a source of the semi-precious gemstone, garnet.

- **Much schist** occurs in the European Alps. Here, the rocks were folded and metamorphosed in mid-Cenozoic times, around 40 million years ago.

- **In Britain**, schist occurs mainly in the Scottish Highlands, where it was formed during the Caledonian Period of mountain building, around 400 million years ago.

- **A period of mountain building** is called an orogeny.

◄ *Schist has wavy bands running through it and this example has reddish garnet crystals.*

▲ *The hills and mountains of the Scottish Highlands are largely made of schist.*

119

Gneiss

▶ *The typical dark and light bands can be seen in this tightly folded gneiss specimen.*

- **Gneiss** is a rock formed by extreme heat and pressure deep within the Earth's crust. Under these conditions any previously formed rock will be completely changed. This is the highest grade of regional metamorphism.

- **During orogenies**, some rocks are buried to the depths at which gneiss forms.

- **Gneiss is characterised** by alternating dark and light colored bands of different minerals. The mineral crystals are large enough to detect with the naked eye.

- **The pale bands** contain lower-density minerals such as quartz and feldspar, while the darker streaks contain denser minerals like biotite, mica, and hornblende.

- **Some gneisses** may have isolated patches of other minerals such as red garnet. These can look like "eyes" in the rock. This rock is called augen gneiss, from the German *augen*, meaning eyes.

- **The composition of gneiss** is not very different from that of the igneous rock granite.

- **Gneiss** is generally the oldest rock in the area in which it occurs, and some gneisses have been radiometrically dated to over 3,000 million years.

- **The major continental** shield areas, such as the Canadian and Eurasian shields, are predominantly made of gneiss, with younger rocks on top.

- **Gneiss** is a very durable rock. Its hardness is exploited in road making, and millions of tons of quarried gneiss boulders are used for coastal defenses.

▼ *Gneiss forms a rugged landscape of low gray hills with much bare rock.*

Eclogite

- **Eclogite** is a rock that forms under high temperature and very high pressure in the deep roots of mountain chains.

- **It is a rare rock** and is important because of what geologists can learn from it about the Earth's composition.

- **Eclogite** contains large crystals easily seen with the naked eye.

- **The minerals** in this rock may be arranged in alternating bands of different types or randomly scattered throughout its structure.

- **Eclogite is a dark-colored** rock made of yellowish or green pyroxene and red garnet.

- **Other minerals** that occur in small amounts in eclogite include rutile, pyrite, corundum, and kyanite.

- **Some eclogites** are found in diamond pipes. They have been taken there from great depth by volcanic activity.

- **Geologists** believe that eclogite gives important information about the rocks at the very base of the Earth's crust, and in the uppermost region of the Earth's mantle.

- **Experiments** have shown that eclogite forms when basalt lava is melted and recrystallized under great pressure.

- **Eclogite** occurs worldwide, especially in California, the European Alps, Japan, and South Africa.

◀ *Eclogite can be a most attractive rock, with masses of red garnet and green pyroxene. This example is from Norway.*

Building stones

- **In most parts of the world,** local stone is used for building. It is often possible to work out what the local geology is like by looking at what buildings, especially older ones, are made from.

- **Some rock types** are especially sought after because they are attractive, hard, or easily cut into usable shapes.

- **Sandstone, limestone,** and ironstone are three sedimentary rocks that are often used for building. Most of these can be cut easily and split along bedding planes. Rock without bedding (massive rock) can be more easily cut into the blocks required.

- **Though granite** is more difficult to cut than some sedimentary rocks, it has been quarried for building stone for hundreds of years. It is attractive and has good internal strength for structural supports.

- **Because stone used for buildings** is often cut and transported in large blocks, quarries developed in the 18th and 19th centuries were usually near good transport facilities.

- **The famous Aberdeen granite** quarries and the granite quarries in the Channel Isles and Cornwall, U.K., were often sited near to the sea to make it easy to transport the quaried rock.

- **Warm-colored limestones** of Jurassic age are used in southern England for many buildings. The well-known Portland limestone was taken to London from coastal quarries.

- **Limestone is readily attacked** by chemical weathering, and many buildings need restoration work when the stone suffers.

- **Slate is a tough**, easily split rock used for roofing.

- **Polished stone** often decorates the facades of offices and banks. Usually, granite or another coarse-grained igneous rock is used for this purpose.

▶ *The body of this cottage is made of small irregular-shaped nodules of flint, found in nearby chalk strata. The framework, window surrounds, and lintels are brick.*

What are minerals?

- **A mineral** is a chemical compound or element that forms naturally in many different ways.

- **Most minerals** form inorganically, which means that living things play no part in their creation. However, some organic materials, such as amber, are usually classed with minerals.

- **Rocks** are made from minerals. Limestone is made mainly of the mineral calcite (calcium carbonate), and granite contains quartz, mica, and feldspar.

- **Some minerals**, such as gold and diamond, are very valuable as currency or gemstones.

- **Geologists** tell one type of mineral from another by using special tests. Many of these are easy to carry out.

- **Many minerals form** as perfect crystals. There is a great variety of crystal shapes, from simple cubes to complex dodecahedra with twelve faces.

- **Minerals** can form irregular or rounded shapes without obvious crystals.

- **Some minerals** are magnetic, others react with acids, and some are too hard to be scratched with a knife blade.

- **As well as occurring** in rocks, minerals form in long narrow bands, called mineral veins, that run through the Earth's crust.

- **Minerals** such as hematite (iron oxide), galena (lead sulphide), and salt (sodium chloride) are important industrial raw materials.

▶ *Minerals can be bright colors and have fine crystal shapes. The yellowish mineral is ettringite that forms as six-sided crystals. Here, dioptase is a rich green color and the crystals have a vitreous (glassy) luster.*

How hard are minerals?

- **Geologists** use a number of tests to tell one mineral from another. The hardness test is very useful in mineral identification.

- **The hardness** of a mineral depends on the strength of the forces that bind the atoms in the mineral together.

- **Gemstones**, such as diamond, ruby, sapphire, and emerald, are very hard. It is difficult to scratch or damage them.

- **Mineral hardness** is measured according to how easily a mineral can be scratched. A mineral is tested by scratching it in turn with objects of increasing hardness, including the minerals on the hardness scale.

- **Geologists** use a special scale for measuring mineral hardness. It is called Mohs scale and was devised in 1812 by the German mineralogist Friedrich Mohs. There are ten points on Mohs' scale, each one defined by a well-known mineral.

▼ *The ten-point hardness scale uses well-known minerals for its reference points.*

| **1** Talc | **2** Gypsum | **3** Calcite | **4** Fluorite | **5** Apatite |

- **Talc** is the softest mineral at point 1 on the hardness scale. One form of this mineral is called soapstone and can be easily carved into ornaments. It can be scratched with a fingernail.

- **Diamond** is the hardest on the scale, at point 10. This highly prized gemstone is so hard that it is also used in industry as a cutting tool.

- **The other minerals** on the scale are: gypsum (2), calcite (3), fluorite (4), apatite (5), orthoclase (6), quartz (7), topaz (8), and corundum (9).

- **Certain everyday objects** are also used for testing hardness. A fingernail (2½), coin (3½), and knife blade (5½) are often used.

...FASCINATING FACT...
The first nine minerals on Mohs' scale have roughly the same gap between them—that is, corundum is nine times harder than talc. Diamond, however, the tenth mineral on the scale, is 40 times harder than talc.

6	7	8	9	10
Orthoclase	Quartz	Topaz	Corundum	Diamond

Mineral colors

- **Minerals** range widely in colors, helping geologists to tell them apart.

- **Mineral color** depends on how light is reflected and absorbed by the elements in the mineral.

- **Quartz**, a very common mineral, can occur in many different colors. Amethyst is purple, citrine is yellow, and the pink form is called rose quartz. Usually, quartz is grey or milky white.

- **Malachite**, which is a copper mineral, is a rich green color, and azurite another mineral containing copper, is bright blue.

- **Common minerals** such as calcite, gypsum, and barite are usually white.

- **Minerals** that contain iron, such as hematite and magnetite, are often reddish-brown or black.

- **Gold** is a wonderful rich yellow color. Fool's gold (pyrite) is a similar color, as is copper pyrite (chalcopyrite). It is easy to tell them apart using other tests such as hardness and specific gravity.

- **Cinnabar**, a sulphide of mercury, is red, as is realgar (arsenic sulphide).

- **For thousands of years**, mineral colors have been used as pigment in paints and dyes. Malachite was used as a green pigment over 2,000 years ago in Egypt.

- **Ultramarine**, a rich deep-blue color, is made from powdered lazurite (lapis lazuli).

▶ *The brilliant green coating on this rock surface is the copper mineral conichalcite. Many minerals that contain copper are green.*

◀ *Cinnabar is a bright red mineral that contains mercury.*

131

Gemstones

▶ *Small crystals of topaz growing into a hollow in an igneous rock. Topaz crystals can be cut and facetted as gemstones.*

● **Gemstones** have been prized for thousands of years for their rarity, color, shape, and durability.

● **There are only** a few dozen types of gemstones in everyday circulation. Other gemstones are too rare or soft to be of much use.

▶ *Ruby is a red variety of corundum and sapphire is the blue form. Emerald is a brilliant green variety of beryl.*

● **Semi-precious gemstones** include many color varieties of quartz, such as purple amethyst.

● **Gemstones** form naturally in many different geological situations. Some occur in igneous rocks, others in mineral veins or cavities.

Ruby

● **Because of their hardness**, gems such as ruby and sapphire are not worn away by erosion in a river and so accumulate in river gravels and sands. These forms of corundum have been weathered and eroded from their original source.

● **Diamond** is the best-known gemstone. Imitation diamonds have been made for many years. Rock crystal (quartz) and glass have both been used, but today materials such as cubic zirconia are produced as diamond substitutes.

Emerald

● **To enhance** their natural beauty, and remove imperfections, gemstones are cut and surfaces called facets are made.

● **A person who** cuts and polishes gemstones is called a lapidary.

Sapphire

● **Gemstones**, especially diamonds, are measured in "carats." A carat is a measure of weight, being 0.007 oz (0.2 grams).

....FASCINATING FACT....
The Cullinan diamond, discovered in South Africa in 1905, is the biggest diamond ever found. It weighed 3,106 carats and was cut into 96 small stones and nine large ones.

Precious metals

- **Gold, silver, and platinum** are all minerals that are precious metals. They occur on their own as "native elements," which means they are not combined with other elements as compounds.

- **Gold** is easily recognized by its rich color and great weight. It is 19 times heavier than an equal volume of water.

- **Gold is a soft metal**, easily scratched with a coin.

- **Found in a variety** of geological situations, gold occurs in veins, often with quartz. It occurs in river sand and shingle, where prospectors "pan for gold."

- **Native platinum metal** occurs as rare, silvery nuggets and minute grains with nickel and gold.

- **Platinum** commands a higher price on the world market than gold. It is used in catalytic converters, oil refining, and jewelry.

- **Silver** is far less valuable than gold or platinum. When clean, it has a fine metallic luster, but this rapidly fades and the metal becomes dull.

- **Silver** forms in delicate twisted wire shapes. Today, most silver is obtained from lead and copper mining and refining.

- **As well as being used** to make jewelry and ornaments, silver is a component of photographic film.

▶ *This small specimen of silver is a mass of interlocking wires. It has become tarnished and lost its bright metallic lustre.*

▲ *Gold is often found in quartz veins. This fine crystal of quartz has small flakes of gold on its surfaces.*

...FASCINATING FACT...
The ancient Egyptians were excellent goldsmiths. The boy king Tutankhamun's collar is made of worked gold.

Mining

- **The metals and fuels** on which we depend are mined or quarried from the ground.

- **Rock** that contains valuable material, usually metal, is called an ore. Hematite is an iron ore and bauxite is an ore of aluminum.

- **Over 3,000 million tons** of metal and mineral ores are mined each year.

- **Ores are finite**, non-renewable materials. It is therefore important to recycle metals after use.

- **Metal ores** exist in many different geological settings. How they are mined largely depends on the size and shape of the deposit.

- **If an ore body is large** and in rocks that are structurally strong and occurs at depth, an underground mine will be used.

- **Surface (open pit) mining** is cheaper to carry out than underground mining. It can also produce far more ore in less time.

- **If the ore** is in loose surface sediments, it can be mined by using high-pressure water jets. Settling tanks may be used to separate the heavy ore from unwanted sand and clay.

- **Coal mining** was once a major industry in Britain, with hundreds of mines. Today, because of the low price of foreign coal and the use of other fuels, only a handful of mines are still working. Coal is also extracted by opencast methods.

▶ *Bauxite is an important ore of aluminum. This metal is strong and lightweight and doesn't rust like steel.*

● **Old mine workings** and spoil heaps are dangerous due to the deep mine shafts below ground. They are, however, often rich in mineral specimens.

▼ *Mines are often in remote places. This small mine is extracting fluorite, which is used as a flux in steel making.*

Looking for minerals

◀ *In the 19th century, gold panning was an important way of obtaining the precious metal. This machine, called a cradle, was used to shake and wash sand that may have contained gold. The heavy grains and nuggets of gold were left behind as the lighter sand was washed away.*

- **Prospecting for mineral deposits** has become a refined science using many advanced techniques. It still relies, however, on certain proved methods, including field mapping.

  - **Field mapping** involves mapping rock structures on the ground. The use of aerial photography and satellite imagery, especially in regions with little vegetation cover, is useful for seeing such structures.

- **Many mineral deposits** are below ground. These can be investigated using what are called geophysical methods.

- **Rocks and minerals** have a property called specific gravity. This can be measured remotely from the surface. Metal ores usually have a high "gravity" and are readily detected.

- **Iron deposits** often have a strong magnetism. In the 17th century, prospecting for iron ores was done using a compass! Modern magnetometers are so refined, they can measure slight changes in magnetism.

- **Geochemical analysis** of river sediment will detect metals that occur in valuable concentrations in the rocks the river has eroded.

138

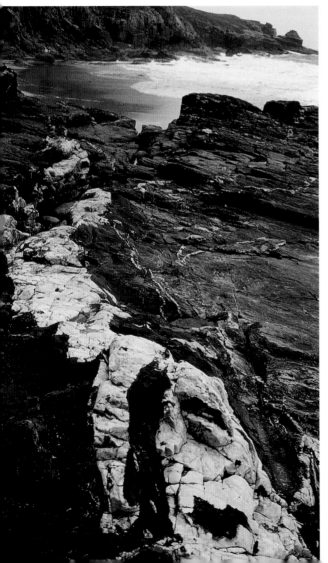

- **Using a scintillometer (Geiger) counter** in the field may indicate concentrations of radioactive minerals such as uraninite.

- **Mineral deposits** may be weathered and altered on the surface. Water that seeps underground can carry minerals and concentrate them at depth.

- **Gold, rubies, and sapphires** found by panning in river sand may indicate the presence of more of these minerals upstream.

◀ *Minerals often occur in veins. Here, a 3 ft (1 m) wide quartz vein runs across dark-coloured slate.*

139

Crystals

▶ *A fine group of small, reddish, six-sided vanadinite crystals.*

- **Many minerals** can form as crystals. These have surfaces that often join together perfectly.

- **Crystals** show symmetry. As a crystal is turned round, the same shape may be seen a number of times.

- **Mineralogists**, scientists who study minerals and crystals, classify crystals into a number of "systems," according to their symmetry. The most symmetrical crystal system is called the cubic system.

- **Not all minerals** that form within a certain system will have the same crystal shape. In the cubic system there can be many shapes, including cubes and octahedra (eight-sided crystals). These shapes share the same symmetry.

- **The shape of a crystal** results from the way the atoms it is made of are fixed together.

...FASCINATING FACT...
In Brazil, giant specimens of rock crystal (quartz) have been found that are as big as a child.

- **Many rocks**, especially igneous rocks, are made of crystals of different minerals.

- **Some crystals** are transparent and allow light to pass completely through them.

- **The way the atoms** of a crystal are arranged may allow the crystal to break along a flat surface. This is called mineral cleavage.

- **Some crystals** break with a rough surface. This is known as mineral fracture.

▲ *Rhodochrosite often forms in banded masses. This specimen shows flat, tabular crystals.*

Other mineral shapes

- **The actual shape** in which a mineral forms is called its habit. This may be a perfect crystal shape or one of a number of other shapes.

- **Mineral habit** is a useful aid to help in identifying minerals.

- **When a mineral** forms no definite shape, it is said to have a massive habit. Lots of minerals, such as quartz and limonite (an iron mineral), have this habit. They can also be crystalline.

- **Rounded habits** are common. Hematite (iron oxide) often occurs as reniform (kidney-shaped) masses.

- **A botryoidal habit** is like a bunch of grapes, with many small, rounded structures. Malachite can occur like this.

- **Native metallic elements**, such as silver and copper, frequently form as wires. These can look like tree branches and this habit is called dendritic (from the Greek word for a tree).

- **Minerals** sometimes form in elongated masses like stalactites. Goethite (an iron mineral) often has this stalactitic habit.

- **Well-formed crystals** that have a constant shape in cross-section are said to possess prismatic habit. A hexagonal quartz crystal is prismatic.

◄ *Marcasite has the same chemical composition as pyrite, but has different forms. This marcasite "sun" is a typical habit of the mineral.*

▶ *Native copper commonly occurs as twisted masses and wires.*

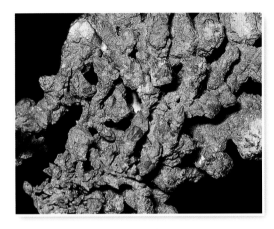

- **Mica crystals** are flat and flaky, rather like a table top. This habit is called tabular.

- **A habit** that looks like a fossil coral is called coralloidal. Aragonite (a form of calcium carbonate) sometimes occurs in this way.

▼ *This is not a fossil plant but delicate patterns formed by the mineral pyrolusite. This is known as a dendritic habit.*

Minerals in rocks

▶ *Feldspar is one of the most common rock-forming minerals. Orthoclase feldspar is often pink in color.*

- **Minerals** are everywhere. All rocks contain minerals and many minerals form as magma or lava cools to make igneous rocks.

- **The elements** in the Earth's crust combine to make minerals, but only eight elements are very common, and these account for over 90 percent of the crust.

- **The main mineral-forming** elements are oxygen, silicon, aluminum, iron, calcium, sodium, potassium, and magnesium.

- **Oxygen and silicon** are very important rock-forming elements, as together they are the basis of the "family" of silicate minerals.

- **As magma or lava cools**, silicate minerals form in a definite sequence. The dense, heavy minerals that crystallize at the highest temperatures form first.

- **Olivine** is usually the first mineral to form, followed by pyroxene and amphibole. Feldspars, micas, and quartz also crystallize in igneous rocks.

- **Many sedimentary rocks** contain minerals that have been eroded from other rocks. Limestone, however, contains calcite, which is formed for the first time in that rock.

> ...FASCINATING FACT...
> Some recently discovered minerals form in
> shipwrecks. Others form in blast furnace slag.

- **Metamorphic rocks** have a number of special minerals in them. These
  include garnet, kyanite, and mica.

- **Certain minerals capitallize** at low temperature on the Earth's crust.
  A group called "evaporites" (which includes halite and gypsum) form as
  sea water dries.

▼ *As an igneous rock cools, minerals crystallize. In this basalt lava, olivine,
pyroxene, and feldspar will be forming as the molten rock solidifies.*

- **Many of the finest mineral specimens** and some of the rarest minerals are found in mineral veins.

- **When rocks break** because of tension in the Earth's crust, faults and joints are formed. Hot fluids from great depths seep upward into these cracks and deposit minerals. These fractures become mineral veins.

- **Hot mineral-forming fluids** are called hydrothermal fluids because they are rich in water.

- **Minerals** containing important metals such as galena (lead,) sphalerite (zinc), chalcopyrite (copper), and cassiterite (tin) occur in mineral veins.

- **Other common** hydrothermal vein minerals are fluorite, calcite, and quartz.

- **Hydrothermal veins** are often associated with large granite batholiths. Hot mineral-rich fluids may form after much of the magma has cooled.

- **Granite** is a rock through which heat rises for millions of years after it has crystallized. Fluids from elsewhere in the Earth's crust may be drawn upward by this heat and many deposit minerals near the granite.

- **A mineral vein** looks like a gash running through rocks. It is often white, containing quartz as the most common mineral.

- **Many minerals occur** in what are called placer deposits. These are concentrations of certain minerals in river sand and silt, especially where the water slows down on the inside of a meander or below rapids.

- **Only minerals** that are very durable and heavy are found in placers. Gold, tin, platinum, and diamonds occur in placers.

◀ *A specimen of blue plumbogummite and yellowish pyromorphite. Countless tons of economically useful minerals come from veins.*

147

Quartz

▶ *Amethyst is the purple-colored, semi-precious form of quartz.*

- **Quartz** is one of the most common minerals. It is widespread and occurs in most rocks.

- **Quartz** can be a great variety of colors. Some of the color forms are semi-precious gemstones. Amethyst (purple), rose quartz (pink), smoky quartz (black and dark brown), and citrine (orange) are all cut and polished for jewelry.

- **Quartz** is the hardest common mineral. It is the defining mineral at point 7 on the hardness scale, and cannot be scratched with a knife blade.

- **Agate**, a semi-precious stone formed in concentric bands, has the same chemical composition as quartz.

- **Chalcedony** is a variety of quartz made of microscopic crystals.

```
....FASCINATING FACT....
The largest quartz crystal ever discovered
was found in Brazil. It was 20 ft (6 m) long
and weighed 48 tons.
```

- **Quartz** often occurs as magnificent crystals. These are six-sided (hexagonal) and usually have six triangular faces, forming a pyramid at the top.

- **Quartz** is made of atoms of silicon and oxygen in the form of silicon dioxide.

- **There are many** ways in which quartz is used. Small crystals of quartz are used in the mechanisms of watches and electronics equipment.

- **Colorless**, transparent quartz is called rock crystal.

▶ *This is a hexagonal crystal of smoky quartz (Cairngorm). It is translucent and light is able to penetrate the crystal.*

Feldspar and mica

- **The group of minerals** called feldspars are the most common minerals in the Earth's crust. Feldspars are generally pale-colored, though some are reddish, bluish, or green.

- **Feldspar** makes up nearly half the composition of basalt lava, which covers the floor of the oceans.

- **Feldspar** is a silicate mineral containing silicon and oxygen. Different types of feldspar have atoms of different metallic elements.

- **Orthoclase feldspar** is a silicate of potassium and aluminum. This is common in granite.

◀ *This glittery mass of mica has typically thin, flaky crystals. Pale-coloured mica is called muscovite.*

▶ *Feldspar is a very common mineral and is commonly white or pale-colored. Amazonite is a brilliant blue-green variety, seen here as fine crystals.*

- **Plagioclase feldspar** has a variable composition. It is a silicate of sodium and aluminum or calcium and aluminum. This feldspar mainly occurs in basalt and related rocks.

- **Feldspar** is used in pottery glazes and glass. It alters to china clay when decomposed.

- **Mica** is a complex silicate containing potassium, aluminum, and iron.

- **Because of its** very glittery appearance and flaky habit, mica is easy to identify.

- **Mica** is common in many igneous rocks, especially granite.

- **Mica has good** insulating properties and is often powdered and used for this purpose.

Augite and hornblende

- **A member of the mineral group** called pyroxenes, augite is a silicate formed at high temperatures in magma and lava.

- **Augite is a dark**, virtually black mineral that helps to give basic rocks their dark coloring. It can also be brown or dark green.

- **Augite crystals** are small, prismatic, and stubby.

- **Augite crystals** make up about 50 percent of gabbro, a coarse-grained igneous rock.

- **Hornblende** is very like augite in appearance. It belongs to the amphibole group of minerals.

- **A very dark-colored** mineral, hornblende can be green, brown, or black.

- **The crystals** formed by hornblende are long and prismatic, often with a fibrous appearance.

- **Hornblende forms** in pale-colored igneous rocks such as granite and porphyry.

- **The metamorphic rock** called amphibolite contains much hornblende.

- **When hornblende and augite break**, different angles are produced between the cleavage. Hornblende breaks with an angle of either 60° or 120° between them. Augite breaks with 90° between the surfaces.

▶ *Hornblende and augite can be difficult to tell apart.*
This hornblende crystal is more slender than typical augite crystals.

▲ *Augite crystals tend to be short and stubby. When they break, rectangular shapes are formed, as in the large specimen on the left.*

Olivine

- **Olivine crystallizes** at very high temperatures in basalts and related rocks.

- **It is a greenish** or brown mineral, which occurs as small grains or crystals.

- **The color of olivine** varies depending on its chemical composition. It is a silicate of iron and magnesium. An increase in iron content gives a browner color.

- **One of the hardest** rock-forming minerals, olivine is almost as hard as quartz.

- **Meteorites** found in Antarctica, belonging to a group called "stony-irons," are made of metal and the mineral olivine.

- **Because of its green color** and hardness, fine crystalline olivine is used as a gemstone called peridot.

- **Gem-quality olivine** comes mainly from Arizona, Myanmar (Burma), and Norway.

- **In basalt lava**, olivine occurs as bright green, rounded crystals studding the rock surface.

- **Peridotite**, a rock which forms very deep in the Earth's crust, is composed of garnet and olivine.

- **Dunite** is an igneous rock made almost entirely of olivine. It has a greenish-brown appearance.

▶ *In this specimen of basalt from Hawaii, there is a mass of pale green olivine crystals.*

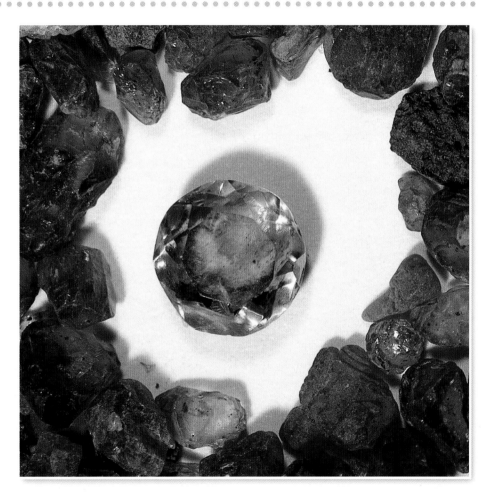

▲ *Olivine can be cut and facetted as a gem stone. This small cut stone is surrounded by water-worn olivine crystals. Gem quality olivine is called peridot.*

Galena and cassiterite

▶ *Galena is a heavy, metallic, lead-gray mineral. It occurs in mineral veins with quartz, fluorite, and calcite.*

- **Galena** (lead sulphide) has been mined since Roman times as an ore of lead.

- **A very dense mineral**, galena is made of lead sulphide, and is 7.5 times heavier than an equal volume of water.

- **Galena** is a soft, gray-colored mineral, easily scratched with a coin. It crystallizes in the cubic system and is often found as near perfect cubes.

- **Lead** was once used to make water and gas pipes because it was easily bent to the correct shape. However, it fractures and produces a cumulative poison that builds up in the body.

▶ *Cassiterite is an important ore of tin, which occurs in veins.*

- **For thousands of years** the county of Cornwall in the UK was a source of tin, extracted from cassiterite (tin oxide).

- **This mineral** occurs in hydrothermal veins, often associated with large granite batholiths.

- **Cassiterite** can be recognized by its dark brown or black color and high density. It is a hard mineral—even a knife blade will not scratch it.

- **About 5,000 years ago**, the Mesopotamians made bronze by adding tin to copper.

- **Pewter**, used much in the past for drinking vessels, is an alloy (mixture) of tin and lead. Tin is used today in solder and tin plate.

- **Today lead is used** in vehicle batteries and as a shield against radioactive sources.

◀ *Today, one of the main uses of lead is for the plates in vehicle batteries. Lead is obtained from galena.*

Iron ores

- **Iron** is one of the most sought-after raw materials.

- **Many** of the sedimentary iron ores of the Jurassic Age in England are now composed of rusty colored limonite. This resulted from the weathering of other iron minerals and concentrated the iron into sufficient quantities to make it workable. In the fresh state, many of these ores were not economic to work.

- **Most iron ore** mined today is found in sedimentary rocks. The richest deposits are in Labrador (Canada,) Hamersley (Western Australia,) near Lake Superior (U.S.A.), and in the Ukraine.

- **Hematite (iron oxide)** is a rich ore. It is a mineral with either a black or a reddish color.

- **Hematite** frequently occurs in rounded, "kidney ore" shapes. The crystalline form is called specularite.

▶ *This 2,000-year-old iron chain was found in a Welsh Lake called Llyn Cerrig Bach.*

▶ *Two different varieties of hematite are seen in this specimen—reddish, rounded kidney ore and black, crystalline specularite.*

- **As it contains iron**, hematite is a heavy mineral with a specific gravity 5.26 times heavier than water.

- **Magnetite** is another rich source of iron. This oxide of iron forms as black crystals or massive, irregular specimens.

- **As its name suggests**, magnetite is magnetic. This magnetism is strong enough to move a compass needle and attract iron filings.

- **Mountaineers and walkers** in areas where the rocks contain magnetite will find their compasses give inaccurate readings.

- **Magnetite** is a hard mineral and can't be scratched by a knife blade.

  - **In Tenerife** in the Canary Islands, there are black magnetite sand beaches, made of iron ore that has been weathered out of lava.

Bauxite

- **Some geologists** argue that bauxite is a rock, not a mineral, because it is a mixture of various materials. These include several oxides of aluminum.

- **Bauxite is usually formed** by the weathering of other rocks rich in silicates of aluminum. This happens mainly in tropical regions.

- **It is an attractive material**, being orange or buff-colored and containing red specks and patches.

- **As well as aluminum**, bauxite commonly contains some iron oxide.

▼ *Bauxite is a dull, red-brown ore of aluminum. This is the most abundant of all metals and much electrical energy is needed to extract it from bauxite.*

▶ *Aluminum is very strong and lightweight. Unlike steel, it does not rust, so it is suitable for aircraft construction. This Boeing 747 is made from many tons of aluminum.*

- **Bauxite** is a very soft material, easily scratched with a fingernail. It is also low density and is only 2.5 times heavier than water.

- **Much mined** for its aluminum content, bauxite is the major source of this metal.

- **Aluminum** conducts electricity well and is lightweight.

- **It is obtained** from its ore by electrolysis. This involves the use of much electricity, which is often low-cost hydroelectricity.

- **Aluminum** is very resistant to corrosion. It does not rust like iron and steel.

- **Because of its strength** and light weight, aluminum is used in the construction industry and increasingly in vehicle manufacture.

Diamond and graphite

▶ *Diamond has been prized as a gemstone for thousands of years. This example has been cut and facetted to show off its sparkle.*

- **Diamond and graphite** are remarkably different forms of the same element, carbon. The properties of these two forms of carbon result from the way their atoms are joined.

- **Many diamonds** may be over 3,000 million years old.

- **Graphite** is very soft, being easily scratched with a fingernail.

- **Diamond** forms small, glassy, often octahedral crystals in the cubic crystal system and is the hardest known mineral.

- **Graphite** forms in flat, platelike pieces with a six-sided outline (hexagonal crystal system). These have a dull, greasy or metallic sheen.

- **The atoms in diamond** are joined in groups of five. These link together in a tight, close structure.

- **In graphite**, the atoms are arranged in layers or sheets that are weakly joined.

- **Diamond** is much prized as a gemstone and is also used for industrial cutting.

- **Graphite** is used as pencil "lead." The pencil industry in Keswick, U.K., was based on local graphite.

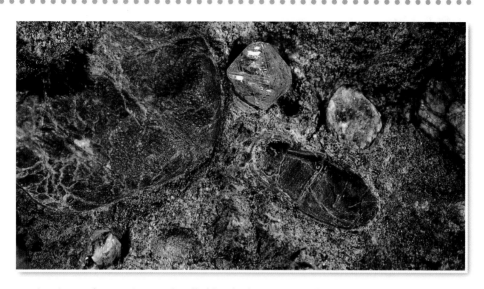

▲ *Diamonds occur in a rock called kimberlite. Two small diamond crystals are in this kimberlite from South Africa.*

. . .FASCINATING FACT. . .
Many diamonds were formed at a depth
of 124 mi (200 km).

Birthstones

- **For nearly 2,000 years**, crystals and precious stones have been linked with months of the year. Different religious and cultural groups have associated different stones with the months. The associations shown here are those popular in western culture today.

- **Garnet**, a gemstone often with a rich, dark red color, and found in metamorphic rocks, is the birthstone for January.

- **The birthstone for February** is amethyst. This is a purple, semi-precious form of quartz.

- **If you are born in March** or May, forms of beryl are your birthstones. March is represented by pale blue aquamarine and May by green emerald.

- **The most valued gemstone**, diamond, is the birthstone for April.

- **June** has an organic gemstone, pearl, as its birthstone.

- **Ruby**, the birthstone for July, and sapphire, September's birthstone, are both forms of corundum, the second-hardest mineral.

- **A gem variety** of the silicate mineral olivine, called peridot, represents the month of August.

- **Opal**, a gemstone with a rich play of colors, which can change as the stone is heated, is the birthstone for October.

- **The third-hardest gemstone**, topaz, is the birthstone for people born in November. Turquoise, a rich blue gemstone, is linked with December.

▶ *Each month of the year is characterized by a certain gemstone. The exact stones representing each month have not always been the same and those used in certain countries are different. The stones here are those generally used today.*

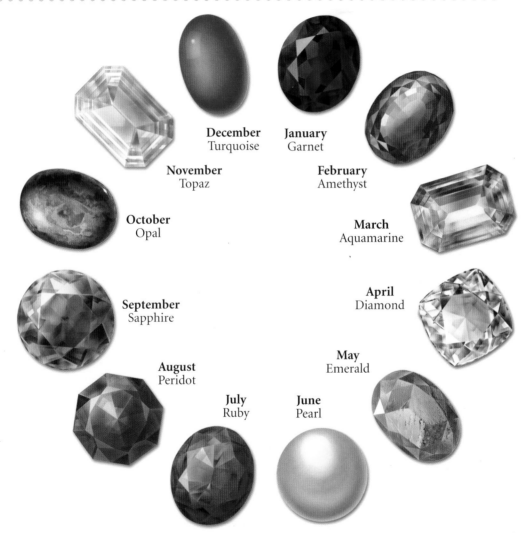

December
Turquoise

January
Garnet

November
Topaz

February
Amethyst

October
Opal

March
Aquamarine

September
Sapphire

April
Diamond

August
Peridot

May
Emerald

July
Ruby

June
Pearl

Beryl and tourmaline

- **These two minerals** are both silicates of various metals. They occur in igneous rocks such as granites and pegmatites.

- **Beryl** is harder than quartz and forms fine, hexagonal crystals.

- **A number** of color varieties of beryl are known, many of which are gemstones. Emerald is the rich green variety of beryl, heliodor is yellow, morganite is a pink form, and aquamarine is greenish-blue.

- **Beryl can be translucent** or transparent, and has a glassy luster (sheen).

- **Tourmaline** is not uncommon in granites, where it forms black prismatic crystals. This type of tourmaline is called schorl.

- **With a hardness of 7**, tourmaline is as hard as quartz. It forms prismatic crystals and may be transparent.

- **There are more** color varieties of tourmaline than of any other gemstone.

▶ *Some of the color varieties of tourmaline.*

▲ *A fine prismatic crystal of beryl in pegmatite. This green-colored beryl is called emerald and it is used as a gemstone.*

- **Rubellite** is pink tourmaline, and the green form is called elbaite. It can also be blue, yellowish, and grey-blue.

- **Some tourmaline crystals** are green at one end and pink at the other.

. . . **FASCINATING FACT** . . .
The largest crystal ever found was a beryl crystal discovered in 1976. It was 59 ft (18 m) long and weighed 380 tons.

167

Opal

- **Opal** is a form of silicon dioxide, but is chemically different from quartz because it also contains water in its structure.

- **The silica** in opal is packed together in minute spheres. Opal is thus a non-crystalline mineral.

- **Opal** occurs in many different forms. It can be botryoidal (shaped like a bunch of grapes), reniform (kidney-shaped) or shaped like a stalactite.

- **Opal** is a well-known gemstone, though it is not of great hardness. Nevertheless, it has a number of attractive features.

- **Because of the packing** of minute spheres in the structure of opal, light is scattered to produce many colors. These vary from blue and green to red and pink. When heated, opal may change color.

- **Another feature** of gem opal is the way it produces flashes of color, which are best shown in curved, polished specimens called cabochons.

- **Opal** forms in certain volcanic rocks, but also often around hot springs.

- **The Romans** considered opal to be a symbol of power and the Aztec civilization valued it as a gem.

- **Today**, much of the world's opal comes from Australia, but some also comes from Mexico.

> ....**FASCINATING FACT**....
> Fossilized trees are sometimes made of wood opal.
> This replaces the woody tissue perfectly.

▶ *This Australian opal shows typical color variation from green to blue. Being translucent, light passes into the mineral and gives the colors depth.*

Geodes and agates

- **A geode** is a gas cavity (vesicle) in lava, usually basalt, which has been filled in with minerals. Quartz in various forms is common in geodes.

- **Basalt lava** erupts at over 1,832°F (1,000°C). As it cools, gas is released and small cavities are left where the gas bubbles were trapped.

- **When basalt** containing geodes is weathered, the geodes, being very hard, are left behind. They often look like lumpy potatoes, but when cut open the wonderful colored bands of agate are revealed.

- **In some geodes**, agate lines the cavity and delicate crystals grow in the hollow interior.

- **Agate** is not made of crystalline quartz. In an agate, the quartz is in minute fibers and grains.

▼ *A true geode has a hollow in its center with crystals growing into it. This specimen has been nearly all infilled with quartz. There is a thin band of agate around the outer edge.*

▲ *This agate shows typical alternating color bands. The specimen has been cut and polished.*

- **Agate** is one of the most varied semi-precious stones. It occurs in many forms and colors.

- **A hard gemstone**, agate is translucent and can be grey, blue, red, green, white, or other colors.

- **Agate** often occurs in bands of different colors. These may be parallel (onyx) or concentric.

- **South American agates** from Uruguay and Brazil are the most common.

- **In Britain**, agates can be found in many places. Southern Scotland is the source of the best British agates. They also occur in the Cheviot Hills in Northumberland, in Cornwall, and on North Sea beaches.

171

Native raw elements

- **As well as gold and diamond**, there are a number of other minerals that are important native elements.

- **Copper** is a metal that occurs as dendritic and shapeless, massive specimens. It is soft and easily scratched, but is very dense.

- **Copper** also combines with other elements in various minerals. One of its main uses is in electrical wiring.

- **Arsenic** usually occurs as rounded, botryoidal masses and can also be found in the form of grains.

- **A group of minerals** called arsenates contain arsenic combined with other elements. Arsenic is poisonous.

- **Sulphur** is a bright yellow element that can occur as fine pyramidal crystals.

- **Sulphur** forms around hot springs and volcanic craters. It often combines with other elements to form the sulphide group of minerals.

- **The element bismuth**, a silvery, metallic mineral that is soft but very dense, occurs in hydrothermal veins and pegmatites.

- **Bismuth** also occurs combined with sulphur as a mineral called bismuthinite.

▶ Native copper is used to make copper wire. This is a good conductor of electricity.

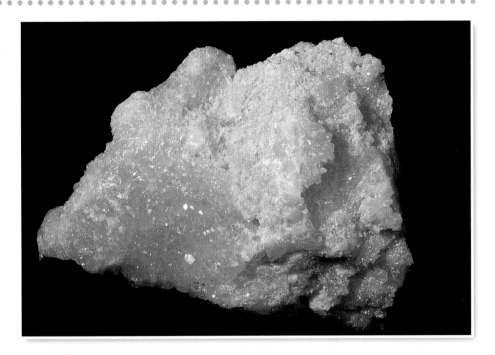

▲ *Sulphur's crystals are clearly visible and are a bright yellow color. This specimen is from Mexico. Sulphur has important industrial uses, especially in the manufacture of sulphuric acid.*

...FASCINATING FACT...
Copper pins and beads have been discovered in the Middle East, dating back more than 7,000 years.

Radioactive minerals

- **There are a few minerals** that contain uranium, a dense, radioactive element.

- **Uranium** combines with oxygen to form uraninite (pitchblende), with copper, phosphorus, and oxygen to form torbernite. It also combines with calcium, phosphorus, and oxygen to make autunite.

- **Uranium** is sought after as a source of fuel for nuclear reactors. Other highly radioactive elements, such as plutonium, can be made from it.

- **Uraninite**, or pitchblende, occurs as cube-shaped crystals or in rounded masses. A very dense mineral, uraninite is up to ten times heavier than water.

- **Torbernite** forms as bright green, box-shaped crystals. These have a shiny surface.

- **Easily scratched** with a coin, torbernite forms by the alteration of uraninite by fluids in the Earth's crust.

- **Autunite** is bright yellow or green and occurs as small crystals and crusty masses.

> ...FASCINATING FACT...
> In 1898, the Polish scientist Marie Curie and her French husband Pierre discovered radioactivity. They identified the elements radium, potassium, and helium in a specimen of pitchblende, a variety of uraninite. Radium from pitchblende is widely used in medicine and industry.

- **Like torbernite**, autunite is easily scratched with a coin and is only of average density.

- **Radioactive minerals** are only for expert use. They have to be stored securely, often in lead-lined containers.

Proton ●
Neutron ●
Electron ○

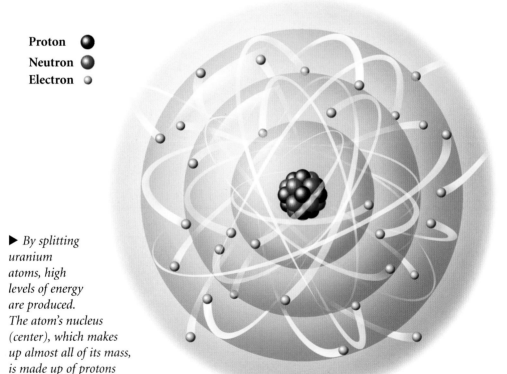

▶ *By splitting uranium atoms, high levels of energy are produced. The atom's nucleus (center), which makes up almost all of its mass, is made up of protons and neutrons. These are held together by a very strong force. By harnessing this force, nuclear energy is made.*

175

Toxic minerals

◄ *Paint pigments are often made from powdered minerals.*

- **Many minerals** are poisonous. The two described here, orpiment and realgar, are sulphides of arsenic and can be dangerous. Because of their remarkable colors, they have been used as pigment in paint.

- **Orpiment** is a wonderful golden yellow color. Indeed, it is so golden that hundreds of years ago, alchemists tried to extract gold from it.

- **Orpiment** usually occurs in mineral veins and around hot springs. Like many arsenic minerals, it smells of garlic when heated.

- **It has** a resinous appearance and forms thin, flaky pieces, or small crystals.

- **The yellow paint pigment** made from orpiment is called "King's Yellow."

- **Realgar** is found in the same geological situations as orpiment. It has a very similar chemical composition, but is a vivid red color.

- **Realgar** has small, prismatic crystals, which often have lines on their surfaces.

- **The surface** of realgar has a greasy sheen. It is a very soft mineral, easily scratched with a fingernail.

- **Orpiment and realgar** are readily available from mineral dealers. They are not dangerous if carefully stored and if hands are well-washed after handling specimens.

- **Over 3,500 years ago,** the Egyptians used crushed realgar as a paint pigment.

▶ *Reaglar is easily recognized by its rich red coloring and greasy sheen.*

◀ *Orpiment is usually a rich golden yellow color. It occurs in mineral veins and around hot springs.*

177

Fool's gold

- **There are a number** of minerals that on first sight have the appearance of gold. Small golden flecks of mineral in a stream bed may catch the eye but after testing are found not to be the real thing.

- **The two minerals** generally referred to as fool's gold are pyrite (iron sulphide) and chalcopyrite (copper iron sulphide).

- **With a few simple tests**, it is very easy to tell real gold from other minerals, and not be fooled.

- **Pyrite** is a common mineral in many geological situations. It occurs in mineral veins, metamorphic and sedimentary rocks, and in some igneous rocks. Fossils are often preserved in pyrite.

- **The true color** of pyrite is silvery yellow, not a rich deep yellow.

- **Gold** is a very soft mineral, which can be scratched with a coin, but pyrite is harder than a knife blade.

- **Chalcopyrite** is a deeper yellow than pyrite and nearer to gold in color. However, chalcopyrite tarnishes on exposure to air to give wonderful "peacock" colors.

▶ *Pyrite commonly occurs as fine, cube-shaped crystals which, as shown here, have striations (lines) on their faces.*

- **Chalcopyrite** is softer than pyrite, but harder than gold.

- **Both types** of fool's gold are not nearly as dense as near true gold. An equal-sized specimen of gold would be far heavier than the impostors.

- **Chalcopyrite** is a valuable mineral, being a very important ore of copper.

▶ *Chalcopyrite is a richer yellow color than pyrite. It is also less hard and can be scratched with a knife blade.*

179

Healing crystals

- **For thousands of years** a number of minerals have been associated with medicine and healing. Minerals such as common quartz are still prized by many people for their healing properties.

- **Early civilizations**, including the Aztecs and Incas, used crystals for their supposed ability to heal.

- **Quartz** is thought to have great healing properties. This may stem from its ability to vibrate consistently. A perfect quartz crystal can allow meditation at a deep level.

- **Sapphire** is believed to be a healing mineral. It is supposedly good for backache and skin disorders. It may also help the spirit and promote contentment and peace of mind.

- **Opal** has had a mixed reception as a healing mineral. It is claimed to induce daydreaming, which may not always be a good thing.

- **Tourmaline** is said to give confidence, relieve nervousness, and promote self-assurance.

- **In Taos**, New Mexico, the Crystal Academy has been set up to promote the use of crystals in healing.

◀ *Sapphire is a form of corundum. It is believed to have healing and soothing properties.*

- **Topaz** is thought to relieve high blood pressure and is also believed to cure insomnia.

- **Malachite**, the bright green copper mineral, may relieve asthma and depression.

- **It is not known** how crystal healing works. It may be related to light reflecting off the crystals having an effect on the body's electromagnetic field.

▶ *Quartz crystals are supposed to have many healing properties.*

Halite and gypsum

◄ *A specimen of slender gypsum crystals. This type of transparent gypsum is called selenite.*

▶ *Halite can form as cube-shaped crystals. These examples are transparent.*

- **These minerals** are both evaporites, formed by the drying up of salt lakes and shallow seas. Halite is a chloride and gypsum a sulphate.

- **Both minerals** are of considerable economic importance, being used in the chemical and construction industries.

- **Gypsum** (hydrated calcium sulphate) is the basis for the manufacture of plaster and plasterboard. It is also used in cement manufacture.

- **Halite,** (sodium chloride) is used in the manufacture of soap, dyes, caustic soda, insecticides, and chlorine. It is also used for de-icing roads.

- **Large chemical industries** are sited in England and Germany, where concentrations of salt (halite) occurs.

- **Halite** can be readily identified by its salty taste. It is usually orange, gray, or white in color, but can be black.

- **Because it is very soluble,** the cube-shaped crystals tend to lose their sharp edges unless they are kept in sealed, dry containers.

- **Halite** is very soft, and easily scratched with a fingernail.

- **Gypsum** often occurs as fine crystals. These can be diamond shaped or long and thin. A form called "daisy gypsum" is like a rosette of tiny flowers.

- **Gypsum** is the definition of point 2 on the minerals hardness scale.

◀ *One of the uses of halite is in the manufacture of soap.*

Calcite and rhodochrosite

▶ *When calcite crystals have flattened tops they are called nail-head crystals.*

- **Calcite and rhodochrosite** are both carbonate minerals. They are made of a metal joined in a chemical compound with carbon and oxygen.

- **Calcite** (calcium carbonate) is one of the most common minerals. It is the main mineral in limestone, and metamorphic marbles are composed of calcite.

- **Hydrothermal veins** often contain calcite along with other minerals, such as galena, sphalerite, and barite.

- **Calcite** is uncommon in igneous rocks. A group of volcanic and magmatic rocks called carbonatites are rich in carbonates. These are rare rocks usually found with syenite.

- **Calcite** defines point 3 on the hardness scale. It forms as sharply pointed or flattened six-sided crystals.

◀ *This type of rhodochrosite, with different colored bands running through it, is often cut and polished ornamentally.*

● **Rhodochrosite** (manganese carbonate) is a rich, deep pinkish-red color. Many minerals containing manganese are red.

● **Rhodochrosite** can form as crystals, but also occurs in rounded or nodular masses.

● **Both calcite and rhodochrosite** dissolve in hydrochloric acid (the acid needs to be warm to react with rhodochrosite.) The bubbles given off are of carbon dioxide.

● **Rhodochrosite** occurs in hydrothermal veins and where rocks rich in manganese have been altered.

● **Because of its attractive color**, rhodochrosite is cut and polished ornamentally.

185

Strange mineral properties

- **Because of their chemistry** or crystal structure, a number of minerals have properties that are special to them, and by which they can be readily identified.

- **A transparent crystal** of calcite is called Iceland spar. When an object is seen through such a crystal, it appears double. This is called double refraction.

- **Many minerals** react with acids. It is best only to test them with weak hydrochloric acid. Certain sulphides, such as galena, release hydrogen sulphide gas when reacting with this acid.

- **Certain minerals** that contain iron are magnetic. Magnetite attracts iron filings. Hematite becomes magnetic when it is heated.

- **Ruby, sapphire**, and some other minerals contain minute criss-cross needles of rutile that produce a shining star shape when light shines on them. This optical property is known as asterism.

- **Quartz**, tourmaline and hemimorphite all develop electrical potential when subjected to mechanical stress.

▶ *Magnetite, as its name suggests, is magnetic. This specimen has attracted a paperclip.*

▶ *Iceland spar is remarkable because it shows double refraction— objects seen through a crystal appear double.*

- **Talc and molybdenite** are flexible and can be bent. Mica, if bent, is flexible and reverts to its original shape.

- **When a mineral** has a high-temperature flame directed onto it, the colors produced are related to the mineral's chemistry. Sodium minerals color the flame yellow, potassium gives a violet flame, and copper colors the flame green.

- **Halite**, nitrate minerals, and some sulphates are soluble in water. Specimens of these have to be carefully stored.

...FASCINATING FACT...
Chatoyancy produces a thin band of light through a mineral, like the structure of a cat's eye. Chrysoberyl, quartz, and moonstone can show this property.

Barite and celestite

▶ *A group of delicate blue celestite crystals. This mineral is an ore of strontium.*

- **Barite and celestite** are both sulphates. Barite contains the metal barium and celestite contains strontium.

- **They can both occur in** hydrothermal veins with a range of minerals, including quartz, galena, sphalerite, calcite, and dolomite.

- **Barite** may occur around hot springs and in nodules in clay. Celestite can be found in evaporite deposits and hydrothermal veins.

◀ *Some of these barite crystals have been colored by iron-rich fluids. Barite is one of the densest minerals found in mineral veins.*

- **Barite is usually pale-colored** and can be white, colorless and transparent, pink, brown, or gray. Fine crystals of barite are common and it also forms rounded masses called cockscomb barite.

- **Because it contains barium**, barite is a dense mineral. It weighs 4.5 times as much as an equal volume of water. This property helps to tell barite from other common pale-colored vein minerals.

- **Barite** is the main ore of barium metal. It is used in "drilling mud," a lubricant employed when drilling for oil.

- **Celestite** can be colorless, gray, white, blue, or green and often forms shiny crystals, like those of barite.

- **Celestite** fluoresces under ultraviolet light, and is slightly soluble in water.

- **Strontium** is used in the manufacture of paint, car batteries, fireworks, glass, and flares.

▶ *The element strontium, which occurs in celestite, is used in fireworks. Strontium gives burning fireworks a rich red color.*

Kyanite and garnet

- **Many minerals** develop during metamorphism. Two of the most attractive are kyanite and garnet.

- **Kyanite** forms in rocks that have been regionally metamorphosed under conditions of considerable pressure and temperature.

- **Schist and gneiss** are the rocks in which kyanite usually occurs.

- **Kyanite** is often various shades of blue but may also be pink, green, gray, or yellow.

- **In schist and gneiss**, kyanite occurs as long, thin, bladed crystals.

- **An interesting feature** of kyanite is its varying hardness. This ranges between 4 and 7, depending on the direction in which it is scratched.

▶ *This fine mass of blue, blade-shaped kyanite crystals is from Brazil.*

- **Garnet** is really the name for a family of minerals. Each garnet has slightly different chemical properties.

- **Garnet commonly forms as crystals** in the cubic system. The crystals are rarely simple cubes, but more usually complex shapes with parallelogram faces.

- **Garnet** can be dark red-brown, green, orange, or red.

- **Because it is harder** than quartz and has attractive colors, garnet is used as a gemstone.

◀ *There are many different named types of garnet. This red-brown variety is called grossular.*

Malachite and azurite

● **Malachite and azurite** have been prized since the Bronze Age for their colors. The two minerals often occur together in mineral veins.

● **Both malachite and azurite** are copper-bearing minerals. They are copper carbonates.

● **Where copper veins** have been altered by weathering and contact with fluids, malachite and azurite may be found.

● **A useful test** for both minerals is applying dilute, cold hydrochloric acid to them. A chemical reaction will occur, producing bubbles of carbon dioxide.

● **Malachite** is a brilliant deep green color, and has been used as a paint pigment for over 3,000 years.

◀ *This specimen of malachite shows the rounded botryoidal habit. Though it is very soft, malachite is cut and polished for jewelry.*

▲ *Small crystals of deep blue azurite coat this rock surface. This specimen is from the Atlas Mountains, Morocco.*

● **As it is a soft mineral** (hardness 4), malachite can be easily shaped and polished ornamentally.

● **Malachite** often forms in rounded, botryoidal masses. When cut and polished, curved patterns can appear.

● **Azurite** is a rich, deep blue color. This mineral has also been exploited as paint pigment for thousands of years.

● **Azurite** occurs in rounded masses and also as short, stocky crystals.

● **With a hardness** of only 4, azurite can be easily scratched with a knife.

193

Fluorite

- **Fluorite** is a common mineral in hydrothermal veins, where it occurs with galena, calcite, quartz, borite, and sphalerite.

- **Because of its chemical composition**, fluorite (calcium fluoride) has some important uses. It is used in the manufacture of hydrofluoric acid and the fluorine chemicals.

- **Fluorite forms cubic** and octahedral crystals. Perfect lenses can be manufactured from fluorite crystals.

▼ *These pale green, cubic crystals of fluorite are transparent, allowing light to pass through them.*

▶ *As well as forming fine crystals, fluorite also occurs in bands of different colors. This polished specimen from China has a thin layer of pyrite on its surface.*

- **In the iron** and steel industry, fluorite is used as a flux. This is a material added to the molten metal to take out impurities and form the slag.

- **In the past**, fluorite was often discarded when mineral veins were mined for lead and zinc. For this reason fine specimens can be found on old mine dumps.

- **Fluorite** is the defining mineral at point 4 on the hardness scale.

- **An attractive banded form** of fluorite, which is found in Derbyshire, U.K., is called Blue John. This is cut and polished ornamentally.

- **Fluorite** is commonly purple, green, or yellowish and the crystals are transparent.

- **Often fluorite crystals** interlock. This property is called twinning. When seen in ultraviolet light, fluorite is strongly fluorescent.

...FASCINATING FACT...
Fluorite is sometimes cut and facetted
as an imitation diamond.

195

Zeolite minerals

▼ This specimen shows fine crystals of the zeolite mineral, stilbite, growing into a cavity in basalt lava. The crystals are 0.4 in (1 cm) long.

- **Zeolites** usually occur in the gas bubble hollows, called vesicles, in lavas. These hollows are left as the lava cools and gas escapes.

- **They are a group** of silicate minerals that have molecules of water in their chemical structure.

- **These minerals** form when hot water and other fluids seep through lava that has been cool for some time and buried in the Earth's crust.

- **Amygdales** are the infilled gas bubble cavities in lava. Amygdales can be made of quartz and agate as well as zeolite.

- **They** have an open crystal structure, rather like a miniature sieve. For this reason, zeolites are used to soak up moisture in industrial processes.

- **Most zeolites** are pale-colored. They usually form good crystals, often in a mass of thin radiating shapes.

- **Zeolites** often occur in concentric zones in thick lava flows.

- **Stilbite** is an unusual zeolite, as the crystals are in sheaflike aggregates.

- **Zeolites are also used** as water softeners, as they are able to exchange ions. The sodium-rich zeolite called natrolite will take calcium out of hard water by exchanging its sodium for calcium.

...FASCINATING FACT...
The "silica gel" found in small packets with cameras
and electrical equipment has a zeolite structure.

Jet

▶ *The modern monkey puzzle tree is a close relative of the plants from which jet formed.*

- **Jet is an organic material** that is often classified with minerals.

- **The term "jet black"** comes from this material, which is often found as layers or discrete masses in sedimentary rocks. It is therefore regarded as a sedimentary rock by many geologists.

- **Much jet** comes from the Lower Jurassic strata.

- **Jet is a type** of coal. It has a high carbon content and is formed from plant material, especially the tree *Araucaria*, commonly known as the monkey puzzle tree.

- **Unlike other types** of coal, jet is found in strata deposited in the sea. Logs and other plant remains probably drifted out into the Jurassic sea, and when waterlogged they sank, to be buried under sediment.

- **The heat and pressure** from overlying layers of sediment converted the plant material into jet.

- **Because jet** is relatively soft, it can be easily carved. It can also be very highly polished and so is used in jewelry.

- **Jet has been cut** and polished since the Bronze Age. The ancient Romans in particular prized jewelry made from jet.

- **Queen Victoria** popularized jet jewelry in the 19th century after the death of her husband, Prince Albert. Jet was extensively mined at that time.

- **Jet has become popular** again in recent years. There are many fake items that are passed off as jet. These are usually made of man-made materials, including plastics.

▶ *An ancient Roman jet bangle. Jet has been cut and worked for jewelry and ornaments for over 2,000 years.*

Amber

- **Amber** is the fossilized resin from ancient conifer trees, and can occur in sedimentary rocks of the Cenozoic Age.

- **Amber** is an organic mineral that occurs as nodules and discrete lumps.

- **As well as** the typical pale orange, it can also be brown, green and black.

- **Amber is very soft** and has a splintery fracture. The surface appears resinous and transparent.

- **Much amber** is found as small pebbles on beaches.

- **It is only just denser** than water and can be carried by the sea. Large amounts of amber occur in the Baltic area.

- **Amber** also occurs in Romania, Italy, France, Spain, Canada, the Dominican Republic, and Russia.

- **Amber often contains** small bubbles. This is called nebulous amber.

◀ *This fossil fly has remained unaltered since it was trapped in resin oozing from a pine tree. The resin is now amber.*

- **Amber** is very easy to carve and for many years has been used for jewelry.

- **Fossils** are often found in amber. These are usually fossils of small insects that were stuck in fragrant resin oozing from a tree. This resin hardened to become amber.

▶ *This necklace and two pendant stones have been made from translucent amber.*

Sapphire and ruby

- **Corundum** is aluminum oxide and is the second-hardest mineral to diamond.

- **Usually**, corundum forms as six-sided (hexagonal) crystals with pyramids at the top and bottom.

- **Corundum** can occur in many colors, including pink, yellow, grey, green, and brown. Bright red corundum is ruby and blue corundum is sapphire.

- **Because of its great hardness** and rich colors, corundum is much valued as a gemstone.

- **Corundum** forms in igneous and metamorphic rocks, but most of the gem quality stones are found in river shingle. This is an example of a placer deposit, where hard resistant minerals have been re-deposited after erosion and transportation.

- **Famous sources** of gem corundum are Sri Lanka, Kashmir, Australia, Thailand, and eastern Africa.

- **Certain rubies** are called star rubies. These show asterism, as small needles of rutile make a star effect in the ruby.

- **Corundum** is used as an abrasive. Emery is an impure form of corundum that often also contains iron minerals.

- **Corundum can be made** artificially. August Verneuil perfected the technique as long ago as 1900.

> ...**FASCINATING FACT**....
> Corundum crystals weighing 375 lb (170 kg)
> have been found in South Africa.

▲ *These ruby crystals from India are in a specimen of metamorphic rock called gneiss. The pale crystals are quartz.*

Decorative non-crystalline minerals

- **Many minerals** that are non-crystalline have great value as ornamental stones, usually because of their colors.

- **The deep blue** lapis lazuli is mainly composed of lazurite. The finest material comes from Afghanistan. Russia and China are other sources.

- **Lazurite** contains veins of white calcite and pyrite. It is about as hard as a knife blade (hardness 5), and is translucent. Lapis is much used for jewelry.

- **Turquoise** is another blue, decorative mineral, though it is generally paler than lapis lazuli.

- **Turquoise can be green** if it contains much iron. Its blue color comes from a high copper content.

- **Much of the attractiveness** of turquoise lies in the veins of darker material that often run through it.

- **Jade** is the name given to the ornamental form of the minerals jadeite and nephrite.

- **Jadeite and nephrite** are as hard as quartz. The green variety of each is the most prized for carving.

- **Rhodonite**, a complex silicate mineral, has an attractive pink color due to the manganese in its structure.

- **Rhodonite** is used for carving and its hardness grading of 6 makes it reasonably resistant to wear.

▲ Green "jade" can be either nephrite or jadeite. These polished examples, and the slab they are on, are made of the mineral nephrite.

Minerals at home

▶ *If you look at grains of salt with a magnifying glass, the small cubic crystals of halite are clearly visible.*

- **A wide range of minerals** and their constituents are used in the home. These range from structural and mechanical components to food.

- **Cement**, which holds the brick or stone of walls together, is made of calcite (calcium carbonate) and mudstone. Cement is mixed with sand, which is mainly quartz.

- **Internal walls** are made smooth with plaster, which is composed largely of gypsum (calcium sulphate).

- **Electricity** is carried through the house in copper wires and water flows through copper pipes.

- **Steel**, made from iron ore (hematite and magnetite), is used for supporting lintels. It is also used to make cutlery, furniture, and many other items around the home.

...FASCINATING FACT...
Accurate clocks and watches use very
thin slices of quartz crystals to keep time.

- **Within the home**, aluminum (from bauxite) is a common metal. It is used in cooking containers, cooking foil and washing machines.

- **Glass** is manufactured from quartz sand. It is melted and shaped into sheets or utensils. Around 2,000 years ago the Romans were one of the first civilizations to make glass from quartz.

- **Salt** in the kitchen and on the dinner table is halite (sodium chloride).

- **Cars contain aluminum** (bauxite), steel (iron ores) and copper. A car battery uses lead plates (galena) to produce an electric current.

▶ *Many domestic appliances, such as washing machines, contain metals extracted from minerals. Aluminum (from bauxite), steel (iron from hematite and magnetite), and copper (native copper or chalcopyrite).*

Glossary

Asterism A feature seen in some minerals when small inclusions cause a shining, starlike image.

Bedding planes The depositional surfaces in sedimentary rocks.

Botryoidal A mineral shape that resembles a bunch of grapes.

Cap rock A rock that traps oil or fluids by not allowing them to seep through it.

Cataclasis The process of mechanical fracture or break-up of rocks during metamorphism or faulting.

Chert A rock made of silica that usually occurs in lumps and nodules in limestone. Flint is a type of chert.

Cleavage surface/plane A flat surface that is produced when a mineral is broken.

Coccoliths Microscopic calcite (calcium carbonate) plates formed in the cell walls of certain algae.

Concordant intrusion An igneous intrusion that follows existing rock structures such as bedding planes.

Continental shelves The shallow sea areas that surround some of the continents.

Continental shields The interiors of many major continental regions, such as Canada and Africa, which are made of Precambrian rocks.

Dendritic Treelike.

Dodecahedral Describing a crystal with 12 faces.

Dyke A sheet-shaped, igneous intrusion that cuts across other features such as bedding planes. Dykes are often vertical.

Echinoids Sea urchins.

Fault A break in the Earth's crust where movement of rocks has occurred on either side of the fault.

Fault plane The surface of a fault where movement takes place.

Habit This term describes the shape of a mineral.

Hexagonal Having six edges or sides, as in the hexagonal crystal system.

Hydrocarbons Compounds containing carbon and hydrogen. Usually the word refers to oil, gas and coal.

Impermeable Not allowing water or other fluids to run through it.

Intrusion A mass of igneous rock that is forced into the Earth's crust.

Joints Breaks in the rocks of the Earth's crust that generally have no movement along them.

Lithospheric plates The plates of rock that make up the Earth's outermost layer.

Luster The way light is reflected off a mineral.

Mantle The layer in the Earth between the crust and the core.

Metamorphose To alter rocks by heat and/or pressure.

Non-porous Not allowing water and other fluids to seep in.

Octahedral Having eight sides or edges.

Oolitic (Ooidial) Describing a sedimentary rock (often limestone) made of minute rounded grains called ooliths (ooids).

Ore A rock containing valuable metals or other economically valuable material.

Permeable Allowing water or other fluids to flow through it.

Placer deposits Sedimentary deposits containing valuable amounts of metals or precious gemstones. They may be river or beach sands.

Porous Allowing water or other fluids to seep in.

Porphyritic texture An igneous rock texture in which relatively large crystals are set in a finer mass.

Prismatic Having a regular cross section.

Radiometric dating Various methods of studying the decay of radioactive elements in rocks, which allow the age of a rock to be worked out.

Reniform Kidney-shaped.

Road stone Broken rock fragments used for road making.

Silicate minerals Minerals made of metallic elements that are joined to silicon and oxygen.

Sill A sheet-shaped igneous intrusion that follows the existing rock structures, such as bedding planes.

Slag The waste material from a blast furnace.

Specific gravity The amount by which a material is heavier, or lighter, than an equal volume of water. Water has a specific gravity of 1. Gold, for example, has a specific gravity of 19.3, so it is 19.3 times heavier than water.

Strata Layers or beds of sedimentary rocks.

Vesicle A gas-bubble hole in lava.

209

Index

Index

Index

Index

Index

Index

Index

Acknowledgements

All artworks are from Miles Kelly Artwork Bank

Photographs from the Miles Kelly Archives:
Castrol, CMCD, Corbis, Corel, DigitalSTOCK, digitalvision,
Flat Earth, Hemera, ILN, John Foxx, PhotoAlto, PhotoDisc,
PhotoEssentials, PhotoPro, Stockbyte
Pages 12, 41, 46, 49, 55, 58, 86, 98, 106, 113, 119, 141, 145,
157, 181, 183, 189, 206, 207

All other photographs courtesy of
Chris and Helen Pellant